Instructor's Guide

for

ENVIRONMENTAL SCIENCE

Action for a Sustainable Future

Third Edition

Ann S. Causey

The Benjamin/Cummings Publishing Company, Inc.
Redwood City, California • Fort Collins, Colorado • Menlo Park, California
Reading, Massachusetts • New York • Don Mills, Ontario • Wokingham, U. K.
Amsterdam • Bonn • Sydney • Singapore • Tokyo • Madrid • San Juan

Associate Editor: Laura Bonazzoli
Production Coordinator: Eleanor Renner Brown
Cover Design: Victoria Ann Philp

ISBN 0-8053-1032-0

ABCDEFGHIJKL-BK-9543210

The Benjamin/Cummings Publishing Company, Inc.
390 Bridge Parkway, Suite 102
Redwood City, California 94065

Preface

This Instructor's Guide is a new ancillary developed to accompany Chiras: **Environmental Science**, Third Edition. Our objectives in developing this guide are several. One is to provide a framework for organization, via **Chapter Outlines**, **Objectives**, and **Lecture Notes**, around which the instructor can develop his or her classroom presentation. Another objective is to provide the instructor with additional material, the **Case Studies**, which can be used to supplement lecture material and/or assigned readings. We believe these Case Studies give added dimension and concreteness to the chapters for which they are included.

In addition, we included **Critical-Thinking Problems** for each chapter in an attempt to help you encourage your students to see the interdisciplinary nature of environmental studies, to analyze the arguments on both sides of controversial issues, and to develop an inquiring, critical approach to learning. We hope these problems will serve as points of departure for stimulating classroom debate.

Another objective is to provide the instructor with **Sample Test Questions** which cover the major points of each chapter. The questions include multiple choice, fill in, and short essay types; where the material does not lend itself to objective questions, only essay questions are included. The objective questions primarily test students' understanding of terms and concepts, or "raw facts." The essay questions call on the students' ability to assimilate these facts into a thoughful response which goes beyond the obvious and memorizable. We hope these samples will provide you with plenty of ideas for evaluating your students' progress in mastering this material.

Finally, we included references to **Suggested Readings** on topics covered in each chapter, and lists of **Films and Videos** which represent samplings of the most current A/V material available to the environmental science instructor. A set of approximately 60 **Transparency Masters** is packaged separately: these correspond to important figures in the Third Edition text.

We believe that a recitation of facts describing the state of the environment is an outdated approach to teaching environmental science. Our aim is to cultivate the students' curiosity, critical-thinking skills, and sustained interest in environmental issues by presenting a much broader and more fully integrated picture.

We hope you share our goals, and that these materials will help you achieve them.

Ann S. Causey

TABLE OF CONTENTS

CHAPTER 1 ENVIRONMENTAL SCIENCE: MEETING THE CHALLENGE 1
Case Study: A Vision of Sustainability 5
CHAPTER 2 NEW VISIONS OF LIFE: EVOLUTION OF A LIVING PLANET 10
CHAPTER 3 PRINCIPLES OF ECOLOGY: ECOSYSTEM STRUCTURE AND FUNCTION . . .17
Case Study: The Endangered Barn Owl 20
CHAPTER 4 PRINCIPLES OF ECOLOGY: ECOSYSTEM BALANCE AND IMBALANCE 27
CHAPTER 5 POPULATION: MEASURING GROWTH AND ITS IMPACT 35
CHAPTER 6 POPULATION CONTROL: KEY TO A SUSTAINABLE SOCIETY 41
Case Study: Help From the U.N. for Population Control 43
CHAPTER 7 FEEDING THE WORLD'S PEOPLE: FOOD AND AGRICULTURE 47
CHAPTER 8 WILDLIFE AND PLANTS: PRESERVING BIOLOGICAL DIVERSITY 58
Case Study: Controversy Over Grizzlies in Montana 61
Case Study: Controversy Over Wild Boars 62
CHAPTER 9 RANGELAND, FOREST, AND WILDERNESS: PRESERVING RENEWABLE
RESOURCES. 67
Case Study: Off-Road Vehicles 69
CHAPTER 10 WATER RESOURCES: PRESERVING OUR LIQUID ASSETS 76
CHAPTER 11 ENERGY: WINNING A DANGEROUS GAME 83
CHAPTER 12 FUTURE ENERGY: MAKING THE BEST CHOICES 89
Case Study: Is Nuclear Power the Answer to Global Warming? 94
CHAPTER 13 THE EARTH AND ITS MINERAL RESOURCES 103
CHAPTER 14 TOXIC SUBSTANCES: PRINCIPLES AND PRACTICALITIES 108
Case Study: Reducing the Need for Animal Testing 111
CHAPTER 15 AIR POLLUTION: PROTECTING A GLOBAL COMMONS 118
Case Study: New Process to Reduce Nitrogen Oxides from Smokestacks 124
Case Study: Noise Pollution 124
CHAPTER 16 WATER POLLUTION: PROTECTING ANOTHER GLOBAL COMMONS 134
Case Study: Road Salt 137
CHAPTER 17 PESTICIDES: A DOUBLE-EDGED SWORD .142
Case Study: MPTP Pollution and Parkinson's Disease 145
Case Study: Controlling the Coyote 146
CHAPTER 18 HAZARDOUS WASTES: PROGRESS AND POLLUTION 151
Case Study: Getting Tough on Polluters. 154
Case Study: Dirty Diapers 155
CHAPTER 19 ENVIRONMENTAL ETHICS: THE FOUNDATIONS OF A
SUSTAINABLE SOCIETY 160
CHAPTER 20 ECONOMICS AND THE ENVIRONMENT 164
Case Study: In Africa, Wildlife Pays Its Own Way 168
CHAPTER 21 GOVERNMENT AND THE ENVIRONMENT 173
Case Study: The New Federalism 177

FILM/VIDEO INDEX 181

CHAPTER 1

ENVIRONMENTAL SCIENCE : MEETING THE CHALLENGE

Outline

I. A MODERN RESPONSE TO THE ENVIRONMENTAL CRISIS
   A. What Is Environmental Science?
   B. Welcome to a New Kind of Science

II. OUTLINES OF A CRISIS
   A. Overpopulation: Too Many People
   B. Depletion: Eroding the Basis of Life
   C. Pollution: Defiling the Land, Water, and Air
   D. The Human Failing: A Crisis of Spirit
   E. Beyond Despair

III. THE POPULATION, RESOURCE, AND POLLUTION MODEL: A NEW PERSPECTIVE
   A. Vital Links: Humans and the Environment
   B. Studying the Interactions: Cross-Impact Analysis

IV. A GLIMPSE OF WHAT IS TO COME
   A. Building a Sustainable Society
   B. Changing Our Ways
   C. The Role of Environmental Science

V. CHAPTER SUPPLEMENT. SCIENCE AND SOCIETY: WAYS OF UNDERSTANDING OUR WORLD

Objectives

After studying this chapter, the student should be able to:

1. Describe *environmental science* as an academic discipline.
2. Identify the trends which have resulted in our transition from environmental *resident* to *manipulator*.
3. See the environmental crisis as a result of several interconnected problems, some tangible (*overpopulation, depletion,* and *pollution*) and others intangible.
4. Discuss the idea that a failing of the human spirit, as evidenced by increasingly materialistic value systems, underlies the environmental crisis.
5. Define *ecological backlash*.
6. Present an argument in favor of adopting an optimistic, rather than pessimistic, outlook on our environmental problems and their potential solution.
7. Describe the role of *system dynamics computer models* in environmental science.
8. Distinguish the importance of *negative* and *positive feedback loops* in the environment.

9. List the features of a *sustainable society* and justify the adoption of new values which will lead to a sustainable society.
10. Identify the role of environmental science in facilitating society's switch to sustainability.

Lecture Notes

I. A MODERN RESPONSE TO THE ENVIRONMENTAL CRISIS
- The *environmental crisis* is a complex of serious social, economic, political, and environmental problems.

  A. What Is Environmental Science?
- *Environmental science* is the study of all of the components of our environment and their interactions; it seeks to understand our impacts on the environment and discover ways by which we can minimize these impacts.
- Ultimately, environmental science can show us how to sustain human society comfortably without unnecessarily or irreparably damaging the earth's life-support systems.
- As a result of the *Agricultural* and *Industrial Revolutions*, our role in the natural world changed from one of respect and cooperation to one of exploitation and dominance.
- Our changing role allowed an increase in activities that have resulted in *overpopulation, resource depletion*, and *pollution*.
- In order to master our environmental problems, we must first learn to master ourselves.

  B. Welcome to a New Kind of Science
- Because it deals with broad-ranging, complex issues, environmental science incorporates knowledge from many disciplines.
- Environmental science is *applied science* (versus pure or objective science) in that it seeks to discover solutions to the most urgent problems facing human society today: the interrelated problems of population, resources, and pollution.
- Because environmental problems are so complex and their solutions difficult and often at odds with conventional wisdom, environmental science and its practitioners are often involved in deep *controversies* and heated debates.

II. OUTLINES OF A CRISIS
- The environmental crisis has four main components: these are the problems of *overpopulation, depletion, pollution,* and *human failing.*

  A. Overpopulation: Too Many People
- At current growth rates, world population will double in 41 years.
- The most serious implication of population growth is increased malnutrition and starvation, especially in developing nations.
- Three key factors are responsible for current population growth worldwide: increased food production, disease control, and better sanitation.

  B. Depletion: Eroding the Basis of Life
- Both *renewable* and *nonrenewable resources* are becoming depleted, largely due to population growth and increasing per capita consumption.
- Poor land management practices have led to severe erosion, deforestation, desertification, and a rapidly increasing rate of species extinction.
- Wasteful industrial processes not only contribute to resource depletion but produce excessive pollution as well.

C. Pollution: Fouling the Land, Water and Air
  - While much progress has been made in cleaning up the most visible forms of pollution, serious threats remain, posed by invisible and often toxic and/or cancer-causing pollutants.

D. The Human Failing: A Crisis of Spirit
  - The environmental crisis is the result of human activities which reflect a *crisis of the human spirit*, general lack of concern for future generations and for planetary well-being.
  - This crisis of the human spirit is manifest in our growing *materialism* and *arrogance* regarding our place in nature.
  - Any attempts to address the technological aspects of our environmental crisis without addressing the human spiritual failings which underlie this crisis will not likely succeed.

E. Beyond Despair
  - *Pessimistic* attitudes are dangerous, since they may thwart efforts to solve serious environmental problems.
  - An *optimistic* outlook will allow us to see our goal, the creation of a sustainable society, as an immensely challenging but nonetheless achievable one. Optimism must be tempered with a healthy dose of realism.

III. THE POPULATION, RESOURCE, AND POLLUTION MODEL: A NEW PERSPECTIVE
  - *System dynamics* has produced computer models which deal with environmental problems on many different levels.
  - One of these models, the *Population, Resource, and Pollution* (PRP) *model*, helps us understand the environmental effects of our activities and may allow us to predict, and thus avoid or minimize, *ecological backlashes* or unanticipated negative impacts resulting from our attempts to solve environmental problems.

A. Vital Links: Humans and the Environment
  - Humans, as well as all organisms, pollute through the acquisition and use of resources.
  - *Pollution* is any change in the environment which could reduce its ability to support life, or which impairs the quality of life.
  - Pollution may be either *natural* (nature-caused) or *anthropogenic* (human-caused); pollutants may be either *biodegradable* (can be broken down by organisms) or *nonbiodegradable*.
  - Some pollutants contaminate only one medium (air, water, or land) while other transboundary pollutants cause *cross-media contamination*.
  - The PRP model shows us how human activities can initiate either *positive* (destabilizing) or *negative* (stabilizing) *feedback loops*.

B. Studying the Interactions: Cross-Impact Analysis
  - *Cross-impact analysis* is a technique which allows us to see and understand some of the many ways in which the elements of the PRP model interact with one another.

IV. A GLIMPSE OF WHAT IS TO COME
  - Environmental science shows us that modern industrial society as we know it cannot continue its present course.

A. Building a Sustainable Society
  - To develop a society which is *sustainable* for now and the future, we must:
    1. *Control* population size
    2. *Use* resources efficiently

3

3. *Recycle* all materials made from nonrenewable resources

4. *Depend* much more heavily on renewable resources

B. Changing Our Ways
- *Societal change* is necessary to stem environmental degradation.
- Necessary changes include adopting a long- (rather than short-) term outlook, abandoning the *frontier mentality*, and replacing our present value system based primarily on personal material wealth with a new one that seeks cooperation with nature, respect for limits, and concern for all species.
- *Technological fixes* cannot solve our environmental problems or extend the ultimate limits set by nature.

C. The Role of Environmental Science
- Every one of us affects the quality of our environment. Our effects can be indirect, resulting from *purchasing decisions* and *lifestyle choices*, or direct, involving action on behalf of environmental quality.
- An understanding of environmental science is essential to all citizens today.
- Unbridled pessimism and unrestrained technological optimism are equally unwarranted and dangerous, since circumstances demand that we act quickly yet cautiously to prevent further unnecessary environmental damage.

V. CHAPTER SUPPLEMENT. SCIENCE AND SOCIETY: WAYS OF UNDERSTANDING OUR WORLD
- An understanding of science is basic to one's education, for science is of value not only to scientists but to all individuals and to society as a whole.

A. Values and Science
- Science is largely descriptive and thus strives to be *objective*; it provides information from which we can prescribe courses of action, which reflect our *values*.
- While values cannot be drawn directly from science, values which serve society's needs will be compatible with and based on laws of science, such as the principles of ecology.

B. The Methods of Science
- The *scientific method* consists of observing, generating *hypotheses*, *testing* to *confirm* or *reject* hypotheses, and generating *theories*.
- *Inductive reasoning* is the type of reasoning most closely associated with science; it involves drawing generalized conclusions from a limited number of observations.
- *Paradigms* represent the underlying basic assumptions of science; when a particular paradigm becomes inadequate, a major upheaval, called a *paradigm shift*, occurs in that science.

C. Critical Thinking Skills
- *Critical thinking* involves careful, logical *analysis* of information in order to reach sound conclusions.
- To engage in critical thinking, one must adopt a *broad, questioning view* of facts, statements, causal relationships and conclusions.
- Most environmental problems are complex in nature and etiology and can best be understood under the *Multiple Cause and Effect Model*.

Case Study

A Vision of Sustainability

The following scenarios helps to create a vision of the future. It is an optimistic scenario, based on a vision of a sustainable society in balance with its environment.

The year is 2050. Two citizens, a husband and wife, are walking to the high-speed commuter train that will whisk them to their downtown offices. They wouldn't think of driving--it would waste fuel. Besides, they are saving alcohol fuel allotments for an upcoming ski trip.

On their way to work they talk about the changes that have taken place in the United States and the rest of the world since their parents' college days in the 1980s. No longer do families have two or three cars; one fuel efficient vehicle is the norm. Many people don't even own vehicles; when they need one for an occasional trip, they rent it. Mass transit has improved nationwide, making the private automobile unnecessary. High-speed trains connect all the major cities. Jets, which burn much more fuel than high-speed trains, are rare; they're mostly reserved for international trips. In the cities, commuter trains have replaced many of the old superhighways.

The city this couple lives in hardly resembles the one their parents used to gripe about. Most families have "gone solar." With climbing oil prices, the solar industry went wild after 2000. Any home that could be converted to passive solar was. Solar panels were installed for hot water. Virtually all homes were retrofitted with insulation and storm windows to prevent heat loss. As a result of the shrinking population and of energy conservation, many local power plants shut down. The public utility companies wisely invested in solar energy and other renewable energy sources.

Recycling has become as ingrained as the throw-away philosophy that dominated the 1980s. Every household has separate receptacles for glass, aluminum, plastics, paper, and kitchen scraps. Separating trash and recycling it have saved enormous amounts of energy and cut down on municipal waste disposal. Water is recycled at sewage treatment plants, or is simply piped to aquifer recharge zones, where it can be naturally purified and returned for eventual reuse. Hazardous wastes have been cut back substantially by reduced consumerism and by modifications in industrial processes, reuse, recycling, and incineration. The tiny amounts remaining are stabilized and stored in well-monitored burial sites.

The U.S. population has fallen. Some demographers think it will stabilize at 180 million around the year 2100. The decline has meant some economic dislocations, but it has also brought many benefits. Nearby streams run clear, the air is much cleaner, parks are less crowded, and wildlife is staging a comeback in forests and wilderness areas. In outlying rural areas, farmers grow a diversity of crops without pesticides or artificial fertilizers. Toxic pesticide residues in fish and birds are almost nonexistent. America's ducks and geese now number 100 million, up 100% from the 1970s. At times, flocks of geese nearly darken the sky.

American agriculture has changed over the years, too. Today, 10% of the farmland is planted in sunflowers, the oil of which is burned like the diesel fuel used in the earlier days. Sunflower oil provides all the fuel farmers need. Farmland also yields large quantities of alcohol for transportation. The food it produces is mostly for domestic use. U.S. food exports almost completely dried up as much of the rest of the world stopped population growth and made tremendous strides toward agricultural self-sufficiency.

Farmers routinely protect their soil from erosion. No longer is half the farmland eroding at a rate faster than it can be replaced. Through concerted conservation efforts, soil erosion is lower than soil replacement rates. The United States is building back its soils. Erosion control has increased agricultural output, stopped the continuous filling of reservoirs, and cut dredging costs in navigable rivers like the Mississippi. Water conservation programs on farms, such as drip irrigation and lined ditches, have cut irrigation-water demands by half.

Drastic changes have come about through careful planning and shifts in basic attitudes. People now have a deep respect for nature and understand that society must abide by its rules; and, most people feel a deep commitment to future generations. The American Environmental Party has dominated the political scene since the late 1990s, when rising oil and mineral prices, among others, began to cripple the American economy. The Environmental Party burst onto the scene with a platform of much-needed changes, which the American public gladly endorsed. Their environmental measures included population control, use of renewable resources, conservation, and recycling. Today, their candidate sits in the highest office, spending a good portion of her time advising other nations how to match U.S. achievements.

The transition to a sustainable society has also occurred in many other nations. Some, like West Germany and Sweden, made significant strides before Americans caught on to the idea. Other nations-- Great Britain, Italy, even the Soviet Union--made the steady transition to sustainable economies. Many developing countries had a rough go of it. Some, like Bangladesh, fell into ruin. Rampant population growth, illiteracy, and poverty made it more difficult for others to make the shift, but progress was made. Today, most countries have stemmed the tide of population growth. In Africa, efforts are under way to reduce population and build sustainable agriculture and industry while protecting the wildlife and forests. Tropical nations have begun to replant rain forests. Small islands of natural vegetation were left intact when forests were cut down in the 1980s and 1990s. These island parks now spread out in all directions, reclaiming the land so carelessly conquered by short-sighted business interests.

Critical Thinking Problems

1. Until quite recently, society has held to the belief that the roots of environmental problems are entirely technological and thus, that the answers to these problems will be found through science and technology. In what sense is it true that science and technology are only addressing the symptoms of a much deeper disorder, a disorder of human values and spirit?

2. It seems that the more informed one is about the complexity and severity of environmental problems, the more pessimistic one is likely to become about our chances of solving these problems without major societal disruptions. However, solutions will not be found in a pessimistic society paralyzed by apathy. How can we avoid excessive pessimism without generating a false sense of security?

Test Questions

Multiple Choice. Each of the following questions has one correct answer. Circle the letter corresponding to the choice that you think best answers the question.

B 1. Which of the following best describes environmental science?

   a. a pure science
   b. the study of population, pollution, resources, and society
   c. the study of the living world
   d. the study of the interaction between technology and population

C 2. Which of the following is at the heart of virtually all environmental problems?

   a. pollution
   b. technology
   c. overpopulation
   d. depletion of resources

A 3. World population is growing at an annual rate of:

   a. 1%   b. 1.8%   c. 2.5%   d. 5%

D 4. At the current rate of growth, the world population will double in approximately _____ years.

   a. 10   b. 20   c. 30   d. 40

A 5. Which of the following is <u>not</u> characteristic of a sustainable society?

   a. relies heavily on fossil fuels
   b. uses wood and other renewable resources whenever possible
   c. practices conservation
   d. recycles whenever possible

Fill in the Blank. For each of the following questions, fill in the blank with the appropriate word or phrase.

1. Oil and gold are referred to as _____ resources because they are not readily regenerated.

2. Unanticipated, adverse effects of human activities are sometimes called ecological _____.

3. Pollutants that are broken down by living organisms, such as bacteria and fungi, are called _____ pollutants.

4. A _____ _____ loop is a cause-and-effect relationship in which one factor shuts off another.

5. The _____ analysis allows one to study the way one set of factors affects another.

Answers: 1. nonrenewable   2. backlashes   3. biodegradable   4. negative feedback   5. cross-impact

7

Short Essay. Write a 250-300 word essay to answer each of the following questions.

1. What are the goals of environmental science and why is this science so different from conventional fields such as biology, chemistry, and physics?

2. Describe the four components of the environmental crisis and give examples of each.

3. Describe the population, pollution, and resource model. Using the cross-impact analysis, discuss how population, resources and pollution affect one another.

4. Describe the basic tenets of a sustainable society and ways in which we must change to be more aligned with these tenets.

5. James Gustave Speth, in "Dedicate the 90's to the Environment," urges the development of a new system of international responsibility. Why does environmental protection today necessitate an international, as opposed to national, response?

Chapter Supplement. Science and Society: Ways of Understanding Our World

Fill in the Blank. For each of the following questions, fill in the blank with the appropriate word or phrase.

1. A(n) _____ is a tentative explanation of scientific observations that can be tested by experiments.

2. The dominant set of assumptions that underlies a branch of science is called a _____.

3. A scientist who comes up with a general explanation of his or her observations is exercising _____ reasoning.

4. In a scientific test of the effects of pollutants on animals, the group that is untreated is called the _____ group.

5. A type of thinking characterized by precision and healthy skepticism is _____ thinking.

Answers: 1. hypothesis   2. paradigm   3. inductive   4. control   5. critical

Short Essay. Write a 250-300 word essay to answer the following question.

1. Why is there so much disagreement among scientists over many issues, such as the effects of pollutants on health? How could this disagreement be minimized?

Suggested Readings and Resource Materials

Barbour, Ian G. (1980). *Technology, Environment, and Human Values.* New York: Praeger Publishers. An excellent examination of conflicting values and interests in environmental decision making.

Brennan, Andrew (1988). *Thinking About Nature: An Investigation of Nature, Value, and Ecology.* Athens, GA: Univ. of Ga. Press. Explores value systems on which the "deep ecology" position rests and examines the position's compatibility with modern ecology.

Ferré, Frederick (1988). *Philosophy of Technology*. New Jersey: Prentice-Hall. Excellent overview.

Gardner, Martin (1981). *Science: Good, Bad, and Bogus*. New York: Prometheus. An entertaining, skeptical look at extraordinary claims, and why they fail to qualify as scientific.

Videos: For ordering information, see Film/Video Index.

Buddhism, Man, and Nature. Alan Watts on the Buddhist relationship between humans and nature. Contact Hartley Film Foundation.

CHAPTER 2

NEW VISIONS OF LIFE:
EVOLUTION OF A LIVING PLANET

Outline

I. ORIGIN OF THE EARTH
   A. Formation of the Universe
   B. Formation of Galaxies and Stars
   C. Formation of the Solar System

II. THE EVOLUTION OF LIFE
   A. Chemical Evolution of Life's Molecules
   B. The First Cells
      1. The Emergence of Microbes
      2. The Emergence of Eukaryotic Cells
   C. The Process of Evolution
      1. Mutation and Variation
      2. Adaptation
      3. Coevolution
      4. Applied Evolution

III. HUMAN EVOLUTION
   A. Our Biological Roots
   B. Human Society and Nature: The Changing Relationship
      1. Hunting-and-Gathering Societies
      2. Agricultural Societies
      3. The Industrial Society

IV. NEW VISIONS: A FINAL VIEW FROM OUTER SPACE

Objectives

After studying this chapter, the student should be able to:

1. Discuss the origin of the earth from the Big Bang to the formation of our solar system.
2. Describe how, according to the *theory of chemical evolution*, complex organic molecules may have arisen from simpler ones.
3. Account for the development of the first primitive cells from non-living protocells.
4. Understand the ecological importance of the evolution of photosynthetic organisms and of oxygen-releasing photosynthetic pathways.
5. Explain the process of *evolution by natural selection* and identify the roles of *mutation* and *sexual reproduction* in that process.
6. Define *fitness, adaptation, coevolution,* and *convergent evolution.*
7. Apply basic evolution theory to modern environmental issues such as *species extinction.*
8. Trace the evolution of humans from their earliest hominid ancestors to their modern form.

9. Identify the major stages of human *cultural evolution* and compare the relative environmental impact of humans at each stage.
10. Characterize the earth according to the vision represented in the *Gaia hypothesis*.

Lecture Notes

- Sustained life is possible only in a system in which all materials are recycled and reused. The earth itself is such a system.

I. ORIGIN OF THE EARTH

    A. Formation of the Universe
  - The universe is believed to have come into existence 15 to 20 billion years ago as the result of the *big bang*.
  - Cooling of the matter expelled into space by the big bang allowed the formation of *atoms* of the various elements from smaller *subatomic particles*.

    B. Formation of Galaxies and Stars
  - *Protogalaxies* condensed out of the matter and separated into *protostars*.
  - Heat and density increased due to the influence of gravity, and *nuclear fusions* began, marking the transition from protostar to *star*.

    C. Formation of the Solar System
  - Our *solar system* began approximately 4.6 billion years ago as the result of a *supernova* exploding and subsequently condensing within our *galaxy*, the Milky Way.

II. THE EVOLUTION OF LIFE
- As our planet cooled, differential migration and settling of elements produced the *core*, *mantle*, *crust*, and *atmosphere*.

    A. Chemical Evolution of Life's Molecules
  - From earth's primitive atmosphere, *inorganic* and simple *organic molecules* fell with the rain and accumulated in oceans and lakes.
  - According to the *theory of chemical evolution*, when exposed to an energy source such as heat, UV light, or lightning, these simple compounds combined to form the complex molecules of living systems.
  - Aggregations of these molecules are called *protocells*; from them, the first primitive *cells* arose.

    B. The First Cells
      1. The Emergence of Microbes
  - The first cells, *bacteria*-like organisms, arose about 3.7 billion years ago.
  - These early cells were heterotrophic; later, *photosynthesis* allowed autotrophs to flourish as existing nutrient supplies dwindled.
  - Over time, photosynthesis released *oxygen* which began to accumulate in the atmosphere; oxygen-using and oxygen-tolerant species now had an advantage and began to flourish.
      2. The Emergence of Eukaryotic Cells
  - The *endosymbiotic evolution theory* explains how primitive bacterial cells colonized other cells, giving rise to *eukaryotic* cells, thought to have arisen 1.5 billion years ago.
  - From these advanced unicellular organisms evolved the multicellular plants, animals, and fungi.

11

C. The Process of Evolution
- *Evolution* is the term applied to the process by which the multitude of life forms arose from a common ancestor.
- The theory which best explains the mechanisms of evolutionary change is called *natural selection*; this theory was first proposed and defended by Charles Darwin.
  1. Mutation and Variation
     - *Mutations* and *variations* due to sexual reproduction give some organisms a *selective advantage* over others.
     - Advantageous characteristics increase an organism's reproductive success and survival and thus cause a shift in the species' *gene pool*.
  2. Adaptation
     - Mutations are *spontaneous*; they do not occur *in response* to environmental change.
     - The *adaptation* of an organism to its environment is indicated by its *fitness* or reproductive success.
     - New *species* form as a result of *geographic isolation* which leads to *reproductive isolation* and, finally, *speciation*.
  3. Coevolution
     - When two or more species exert selective pressure on one another, the result is *coevolution*.
  4. Applied Evolution
     - An understanding of evolution is essential for students of environmental science, since humans act as powerful selective agents, interfering with the process of evolution, and sometimes destroying its products.

III. HUMAN EVOLUTION

A. Our Biological Roots
   - The first *hominids*, *australopithecines*, appeared 4 million years ago in southern Africa.
   - Subsequently, *Homo habilis*, *H. erectus*, and *H. sapiens* emerged.

B. Human Society and Nature: The Changing Relationship
   - *Cultural evolution* has produced the major social groupings of human societies.
   - All human societies have impacted the environment, the extent of the impact depending on the society's population size, resource demand, and choice of resources for support.
   1. Hunting-and-Gathering Societies
      - For most of our history, humans have lived in *hunting-and-gathering societies*.
      - Though not always environmentally benign, these societies, due to their low population size and primitive technology, had little permanent impact on the environment.
   2. Agricultural Societies
      - The *Agricultural Revolution* occurred around 8000 B.C., beginning probably in Southeast Asia.
      - Domestication of plants and animals allowed populations to increase, cities to develop, and humans to change their relationship with nature from one of *cooperation and respect* to one of *domination and exploitation*.
   3. The Industrial Society
      - This society rose to prominence out of the *Industrial Revolution* of the 18th and 19th Centuries.
      - Increasing *mechanization*, new *technology*, advances in *medicine*, and improved *sanitation* all set the stage for rapid population growth and corresponding environmental deterioration.

- *Advanced industrial societies* arose after WWII; these societies are noted for high levels of *production/consumption*, heavy reliance on *synthetics* and *nonrenewables*, and increasing per capita *energy demand*.
- Increasing *specialization* in advanced societies narrows our thinking, increases our dependency and vulnerability, and further alienates us from nature.

IV. NEW VISIONS: A FINAL VIEW FROM OUTER SPACE
- The *Gaia hypothesis* proposes that the earth is a living organism which maintains conditions different from those we would expect of a nonliving system.

Critical Thinking Problems

1. In response to modern society's increasing alienation from nature, many environmental writers and activists are calling for a "back-to-the-land" movement. Do you think we can achieve this goal and still maintain our current standard of living? Defend your answer.

2. How might one be able to use the Gaia hypothesis to argue that we need *not* make sacrifices to protect the earth?

Test Questions

Multiple Choice. Each of the following questions has one correct answer. Circle the letter corresponding to the choice you think best answers the question.

E   1. During the formation of the universe:

   a. stable atoms did not form until 1 million years after the fiery explosion.
   b. huge clouds of matter began to form about four billion years ago and these gave rise to the planets.
   c. protogalaxies formed from cosmic dust and gave rise to stars and planets.
   d. stars formed early on from the hot gases in space.
   e. a & c
   f. b & d

B   2. The chemist who first demonstrated that biological molecules could be synthesized from inorganic molecules abiotically is:

   a. Oparin.
   b. Miller.
   c. Fox.
   d. Watson.

A   3. The first cells:

   a. arose at least 3.7 billion years ago.
   b. contained genetic material in nuclei.
   c. probably resembled amoebas.
   d. contained chlorophyll.

A   4. The theory of evolution:

    a. describes how new species are formed through random genetic changes and natural selection.
    b. describes how an organism in a population meets changing circumstances.
    c. was first outlined by Charles Darwin.
    d. a & b
    e. a & c
    f. b & c

B   5. Which of the following is true regarding primate evolution?

    a. Humans evolved from the tree shrew about 4 million years ago in Africa.
    b. The tree shrew gave rise to the tree-dwelling primates about 50 million years ago.
    c. The first hominids (humans and their fossil relatives) arose directly from the tree shrew.
    d. *Homo sapiens* was the first tool maker.

D   6. Cro-Magnons:

    a. emerged 30,000 years ago, probably in Africa.
    b. rapidly replaced the Asiatic and European Neanderthals.
    c. may have had a fully developed language.
    d. all of the above
    e. none of the above

A   7. Hunters and gatherers:

    a. generally caused little permanent damage to the environment because their numbers were small.
    b. lived unhealthy lives constantly in search of food.
    c. developed a thorough knowledge of crops they could grow for food.
    d. were responsible for widespread deforestation, especially in the fertile crescent.

D   8. Which of the following is *not* a characteristic of modern factories?

    a. energy intensive
    b. often rely on nonrenewable resources
    c. efficient usually only on a large scale
    d. use small to medium-sized machines to maximize human input

Fill in the Blank. For each of the following questions, fill in the blank with the appropriate word or phrase.

1. The _____ _____ theory describes the origin of the Universe.

2. Sandwiched between the core and crust of the earth is a layer called the _____ .

3. The theory of _____ _____ says that organic compounds necessary for the earliest living cells were produced from inorganic materials in the earth's primitive atmosphere.

4. _____ is a process by which plants capture sunlight energy and use it, along with atmospheric carbon dioxide, to synthesize organic molecules such as sugar.

14

5. The theory of _____ _____ explains how the first cellular organelles arose.

6. A barrier, such as a mountain range or river, that splits an organism's range results in _____ isolation.

7. The tendency of organisms to develop the same types of adaptations in response to similar environmental conditions is _____ evolution.

8. A change in the genetic material, the DNA, resulting from radiation or a chemical in the environment is called a _____.

9. Sections of the DNA that regulate specific functions are called _____.

10. The genetic composition of a population is called its _____ _____.

11. The notion that genetic changes accumulate over many millions of years to produce a new species is called_____.

Answers: 1. big bang   2. mantle   3. chemical evolution   4. Photosynthesis   5. endosymbiotic evolution   6. geographic   7. convergent   8. mutation   9. genes   10. gene pool   11. gradualism

Short Essay. Write a 250-300 word essay to answer each of the following questions.

1. Describe how a solar system forms. Be sure to include the terms protogalaxy, protostar, and supernova.

2. Using your knowledge of evolution, predict what changes may occur in the anatomy and physiology of modern humans in the next one million years. Be certain to discuss your reasons for new adaptations.

3. Describe how natural selection works and why it can lead to the formation of new species, adaptive radiation, and coevolution.

4. Briefly summarize the major changes in the human-environment interaction during human cultural evolution. How were hunting and gathering, agricultural, and industrial societies alike in this regard and how were they different? Do you see any dangerous trends during the cultural evolution of human society?

Suggested Readings and Resources Materials

Bronowski, Jacob Jr. (1974). *The Ascent of Man.* Boston: Little, Brown. Excellent overview of all stages of human cultural evolution.

Gould, Stephen Jay (1989). *Wonderful Life.* New York: Norton. Challenges the conventional wisdom about the relationship between evolution and species diversity.

Lovelock, J.E. (1987). *Gaia: A New Look At Life On Earth.* New York: Oxford.

Smith, John Maynard, Ed. (1983). *Evolution Now.* San Francisco: W.H. Freeman. Good essays on modern evolution theory; includes a section devoted to the gradualism-vs-punctuated equilibrium debate.

WorldWatch Institute (1990). *State of the World.* Washington: WorldWatch Institute. Tells us where we are today on the path towards a sustainable society.

Videos: For ordering information, see Film/Video Index.

Can Man Survive? Examines the threats to man due to his own cultural evolution. Contact Films for the Humanities & Sciences, Inc.

Evolution: The Evidence for Modern Ideas on Evolution. An 11-video series, with several especially relevant segments, including: *Structural Homologies and Co-Evolution, The Evolution of Man, Selection and Adaptation,* and *The Human Influence.* Contact Films for the Humanities & Sciences, Inc.

Gaia: The Living Planet. The Gaia hypothesis; interviews with James Lovelock. Contact Bullfrog Films.

Gorilla, Gorilla, Gorilla. A closeup look at the behavior patterns, social interactions, and threatened survival of one of our closest evolutionary relatives. Contact University of California Extension Media Center.

The Blue Planet. Explains the development of life on earth and how earth's environment shaped the evolution of its life forms. Contact Films for the Humanities & Sciences, Inc.

On the Edge of Paradise. Shows the environmental effects of rapid development and resource depletion in the Caribbean. Contact BBC Enterprises.

CHAPTER 3

PRINCIPLES OF ECOLOGY:
ECOSYSTEM STRUCTURE AND FUNCTION

Outline

I. HOW IS THE LIVING WORLD ORGANIZED?
   A. The Biosphere
   B. Biomes
   C. Aquatic Life Zones
   D. Ecosystems
      1. Abiotic Factors
      2. Biotic Factors
   E. Habitat and Niche

II. HOW DO ECOSYSTEMS WORK?
   A. Food Chains and Food Webs
      1. Classifying Consumers
   B. The Flow of Energy and Matter Through Ecosystems
      1. What is Energy?
      2. The First Law
      3. The Second Law
      4. Entropy
      5. Biomass and Ecological Pyramids
      6. Productivity
   C. Nutrient Cycles
      1. The Carbon Cycle
      2. The Nitrogen Cycle
      3. The Phosphorus Cycle

III. CHAPTER SUPPLEMENT. THE BIOMES

Objectives

After studying this chapter, the student should be able to:

1. Define *biosphere, biome,* and *ecosystem.*
2. List several *abiotic* and several *biotic* ecosystem components and discuss the influence of the former on the latter.
3. Name and describe the various *relationships* between species and between members of one species.
4. Differentiate *habitat* and *niche.*
5. Discuss the relevance of the *competitive exclusion principle* to modern wildlife problems stemming from species introductions and extinctions.
6. Diagram and label the *trophic levels* of a typical *food web.*
7. Relate the *laws of thermodynamics* to modern energy and agricultural problems.

17

8. Describe the three major *biogeochemical cycles* and identify the ways by which humans can interfere with each of these.
9. List the major *biomes* and, for each, give distinguishing *characteristics* and identify the major *threats*.
10. Discuss the idea that much of our environmental destruction is due to our underlying personal insecurity and misguided attempts to deal with it.

Lecture Notes

- *Ecology* is the study of organisms and their relationships to one another and to the environment.

I. HOW IS THE LIVING WORLD ORGANIZED?

A. The Biosphere
  - *Biosphere* or *ecosphere* refers to the life-supporting portion of the earth.
  - The biosphere is a *closed system* because within it all materials are recycled and reused. Humans break these cycles at great risk.

B. Biomes
  - *Biomes* are terrestrial areas with distinctive *climate, soil characteristics*, and *plant and animal associations*.

C. Aquatic Life Zones
  - These zones, similar to biomes, are determined primarily by *sunlight* penetration and *nutrient* availability.
  - *Reefs, estuaries, deep ocean areas*, and *continental shelves* are distinct aquatic life zones.

D. Ecosystems
  - *Ecosystems*, or *ecological systems*, are dynamic networks of interdependent plants and animals in a particular environment.
  - *Ecotones* are transitional areas of overlap between adjacent ecosystems.
  - All ecosystem components are either *biotic* (living) or *abiotic* (nonliving).
  1. Abiotic Factors
    - These include *sunlight, physical factors*, and *chemical components*.
    - Each organism can thrive only within the limits of its *range of tolerance* to abiotic factor fluctuation.
    - The *limiting factor* is that abiotic element, such as rainfall, temperature, or nitrate, primarily responsible for restricting the growth or reproduction of key organisms in an ecosystem.
  2. Biotic Factors
    - These include all living things in an ecosystem.
    - Groups of the same species in an area form a *population*; several populations living together form a *community*.
    - Organisms within a community may interact through *predation, commensalism, mutualism, neutralism, parasitism*, or *inter-/intraspecific competition*.

E. Habitat and Niche
  - *Habitat* is an organism's environment; *niche* describes an organism's ecological role in that environment.
  - The *exclusion principle* states that, due to interspecific competition, no two species can successfully occupy the same niche.

II. HOW DO ECOSYSTEMS WORK?

A. Food Chains and Food Webs
   - Each organism is either a *producer* (or *autotroph,* self-feeder) or a *consumer* (or *heterotroph,* other-feeder).
   - Depending on their primary feeding habits, consumers may be classified as *herbivores, carnivores,* or *omnivores.*
   - A *food chain* is a series of organisms, each feeding on the preceding.
   - Food chains may be either the *grazer* or *decomposer* (detritus) type.
   1. Classifying Consumers
      - Organisms occupy feeding or *trophic levels.* The first trophic level is occupied by producers; the second, third, and subsequent levels are occupied by consumers.
      - *Food web* is a term which more accurately describes the feeding relationships in an ecosystem.

B. The Flow of Energy and Matter Through Ecosystems
   - All ecosystems ultimately depend on *photosynthesis* by green plants for their energy.
   1. What is Energy?
      - *Energy* is the capacity to do work.
      - Energy is either *potential* or *kinetic,* and always follows the laws of *thermodynamics.*
   2. The First Law
      - This is the law of *conservation of energy:* energy can be neither created nor destroyed, only transformed.
   3. The Second Law
      - States that any conversion *degrades* energy in quality.
   4. Entropy
      - Without energy input, *entropy* or disorder must always increase.
   5. Biomass and Ecological Pyramids
      - Dry organic matter produced by living things is termed *biomass.*
      - Little biomass, usually 5-20% actually passes from one trophic level to the next. As a result, graphic representations of ecosystems show *pyramids* of *biomass, energy,* or *numbers.* These pyramids have important *ecological* and *human implications.*
   6. Productivity
      - Ecosystem productivity is measured as *gross* or *net primary productivity,* in Kcal/m^2/year.

C. Nutrient Cycles
   - Nutrients move through the biosphere in *biogeochemical cycles.*
   - Each cycle involves an *environmental* and an *organismic* phase.
   1. The Carbon Cycle
      - *Photosynthesis* and *cellular respiration* (an oxidative process) cycle carbon and oxygen in the biosphere.
      - Humans affect the carbon cycle by *deforestation* (reducing photosynthesis) and *burning* (oxidizing) fossil fuels.
   2. The Nitrogen Cycle
      - Atmospheric nitrogen is made available to plants by a variety of organisms capable of *nitrogen fixation.*
      - Modern *farming* practices are interfering with the natural cycling of nitrogen.
   3. The Phosphorus Cycle
      - *Phosphorus-rich rocks* slowly release phosphates to soils and water.
      - Artificial fertilizers replace phosphates lost to runoff; this practice often causes pollution problems in nearby aquatic systems.

III. CHAPTER SUPPLEMENT. THE BIOMES

A. Tundra
- This is the northernmost and largest biome.
- Characterized by *low precipitation* (<10"/year), extreme *cold*, *permafrost*, and *treelessness*.
- Low species diversity is partially responsible for the tundra's *fragility*.

B. Taiga
- Consists of coniferous forests south of the tundra.
- The major threats to the taiga have included *trapping* and *clearcutting*.

C. Temperate Deciduous Forest
- Occupies the *eastern United States, Europe*, and *northeastern China*.
- Characterized by *mild* climate, ample *rainfall*, and *broadleaved trees*.
- Major threats include *erosion* and *deforestation*.

D. Grassland
- Forms in response to *limited water* (usually 10-30"/year) in continental interiors; has some of the *richest soils* on earth.
- Grasslands are damaged by *cultivation* and excessive *grazing*.

E. Desert
- Found on most continents; distinguished by *low rainfall* (generally <10"/year).
- This relatively *fragile* biome is threatened in the U.S. by uncontrolled growth in population and water demand of cities, and elsewhere by overgrazing and deforestation.

F. Tropical Rain Forest
- A *complex* biome with *little seasonal temperature fluctuation* and over 80" of rain/year.
- Though the soil is *nutrient-poor*, tropical rain forests support a higher diversity of species than do any other biomes.
- *Deforestation* is destroying this biome at an alarming rate.

G. Altitudinal Biomes
- These result from rainfall and temperature variations similar to those associated with latitude.

Case Study

The Endangered Barn Owl: Ecosystem Balance and Habitat Destruction

Barn owls are extraordinary mousetraps. One Utah biologist watched a pair of barn owls deliver 21 rodents to their nestlings in just 25 minutes. Bruce Colving, a barn owl researcher at Ohio's Bowling Green University concludes that a pair of nesting owls and a brood of six will eat approximately 1,000 small animals during the breeding season. Most of these are rodents -- mice, rats, gophers, and squirrels.

Because they are an excellent mousetrap, many farmers welcome the barn owl. Farmers, in fact, often build nest boxes to attract the birds. Unfortunately, in the heartland of the United States, the barn owl is in deep trouble. The bird is endangered in seven midwestern states (Illinois, Indiana, Iowa, Michigan, Missouri, Ohio, and Wisconsin).

The reason for the demise of the barn owl is not known, but there are several suspect factors. First is the demolition of old barns and silos which are often used as nesting sites. Pesticides, which are used to kill mice, may also be partly responsible for the loss of owls. An increase in the region's population of great horned owls, which prey on the smaller barn owl, may also be part of the equation.

Research on barn owls shows that one of the most probable causes of the population decline is habitat destruction. The loss of grasslands and meadows, say some researchers, is one of the dominant factors in the decline of this owl. In areas where grasslands and meadows remain intact, the barn owl thrives. In areas where they have been destroyed, these birds vanish.

Grassland is important to the barn owl because it is the home of abundant prey. Voles, small mouselike rodents, make up 70% of the barn owl's diet. Without grasslands, few voles survive. Research shows a direct link between the number of barn owls and federal farm programs that encourage farmers to take land out of production, letting grassland replace crops. Since the 1930s, the barn owl population has oscillated in concert with federal crop programs. When land is taken out of production, barn owl populations increase. When it is put into production, barn owl populations fall.

As is true of many predators, the success of the barn owl is linked to the availability of prey. When abundant prey is available, barn owls can mate as early as 7 months of age. They can produce clutches of up to 10 eggs. In years of abundance, barn owls often produce two clutches. However, when voles are scarce, the birds lay few eggs, and in some cases may not nest at all.

Barn owls have exceptional night vision. This enables them to find prey in near total darkness. The bird's concave face also acts as a sound-collecting disk. Even the faint rustling of voles beneath a mat of grass can be detected. Furthermore, the birds' wing feathers have a unique structure that allows them to approach their prey without sound.

To protect the barn owl, private individuals and farmers throughout the Midwest continue to erect nesting boxes. But most experts agree that the best conservation strategy is to protect habitat.

Source: Adapted from *National Wildlife*, Vol. 26, No. 4, June-July, 1988, pp. 40-44.

Critical Thinking Problems

1. Some people claim that we have a moral obligation to feed as many of our fellow humans as we can. If so, are we in the developed nations morally obligated to stop eating meat and to become vegetarians? Keep the concept of ecological pyramids in mind when considering this question.

2. To what extent do you feel that pursuit of material well-being fills a "psychological void" in our lives? Is there any way to fill this void, if it exists, within a sustainable society?

Test Questions

Multiple Choice. Each of the following questions has one correct answer. Circle the letter corresponding to the choice you think best answers the question.

B   1. Regarding the concept of the ecological niche, which of the following is true?

    a. Two species can occupy identical niches, usually with only a small amount of competition.
    b. The niche describes where an organism lives and all its interactions with living and nonliving components of an ecosystem.
    c. The niche is essentially the same as an organism's habitat, so the terms can be used interchangeably.
    d. none of the above

C   2. Which term(s) best describe(s) humans?

    a. autotrophs
    b. producer organisms
    c. heterotrophs
    d. decomposers
    e. a & b
    f. a & c

C   3. The zebra and bison occupy the same niche but on different continents. Because of this, these organisms are considered:

    a. predators.
    b. grazers.
    c. ecological equivalents.
    d. autotrophs.

D   4. Which organisms are microconsumers?

    a. blue-green algae
    b. fungi
    c. bacteria
    d. b & c
    e. a & b

A   5. Which of the following is true?

    a. Plant and animal remains are the source of organic matter in the detritus food chain.
    b. Those organisms that are first on the grazing food chain are called primary consumers.
    c. Autotrophs are usually located on the second and third trophic levels.
    d. The food chain provides a way for energy to be recycled.

B   6. The first law of thermodynamics states:

    a. all systems move toward maximum disorder.
    b. energy is neither created nor destroyed.
    c. energy is degraded when it changes forms.
    d. energy transformations are rare.

D 7. Why is biomass at the second trophic level in most ecosystems not as great as biomass at the first trophic level?

a. Not all of the plant matter is eaten by organisms on the second trophic level.
b. Not all of the biomass eaten by herbivores is digested.
c. Some of the biomass is used to make cellular energy and body heat.
d. all of the above
e. none of the above

C 8. Which of the following is a consequence of decreasing energy and biomass as one proceeds toward the top of the food chain?

a. The size of the organisms decreases.
b. The number of organisms increases.
c. The number of organisms decreases.
d. The number of organisms stays the same.

A 9. Why can more people be supported by eating vegetables and grains from a field than by eating meat from beef grazed on the same land?

a. The lower an organism feeds on a food chain, the greater the available biomass.
b. This statement is ridiculous; it's the other way around.
c. Beef biomass is not converted into human flesh as efficiently as plant biomass.
d. none of the above

C 10. The second law of thermodynamics states:

a. energy is neither created nor destroyed, simply converted from one form to another.
b. energy is destroyed when it is converted from one form to another.
c. when energy is converted from one form to another, it is always degraded.
d. all systems proceed toward maximum order.

B 11. Which of the following is (are) true regarding biomass?

a. It is a form of kinetic energy
b. In an ecosystem, the biomass usually decreases the higher one goes in the food chain.
c. Biomass is the net weight of all organisms at each trophic level.
d. none of the above

E 12. The conversion of atmospheric nitrogen into inorganic nitrogen:

a. occurs in the roots of all plants.
b. is called nitrogen fixation.
c. occurs in nitrogen nodules in legumes, such as peas.
d. takes place in fungi.
e. b & c

D   13. A lump of coal and a starch molecule have what in common?

       a. They both contain work.
       b. Neither has the capacity to do work.
       c. They are inorganic molecules.
       d. They are both forms of potential energy.

F   14. Carbon enters the atmosphere:

       a. primarily as a byproduct of photosynthesis.
       b. as a byproduct of bacterial decomposition of detritus.
       c. when plant materials are burned.
       d. through the combustion of fossil fuels.
       e. a, b & c
       f. b, c & d

Fill in the Blank. For each of the following questions, fill in the blank with the appropriate word or phrase.

1.   That part of the earth which supports life is called the _____ .

2.   Any system that must recycle its components over and over to continue functioning is called a(n) _____ system.

3.   The tundra and desert are examples of _____ .

4.   The abiotic factor that outweighs all others necessary for growth in an ecosystem is called a _____ factor.

5.   The zone between adjacent ecosystems is called an _____ .

6.   Thermal shock, which kills fish populations, is an example of water temperature exceeding the _____ _____ _____ .

7.   Sulfur, nitrogen and carbon are called _____ because they are required in large quantities by living things.

8.   A measure of the total amount of biomass produced in an ecosystem is the _____ _____ productivity.

9.   A grizzly bear eats a grass-eating marmot. The grizzly is on the _____ trophic level in this food chain.

10. In the same example, the grizzly is a _____ consumer.

Answers: 1. biosphere 2. closed 3. biomes 4. limiting 5. ecotone 6. range of tolerance
7. macronutrients 8. gross primary 9. third 10. secondary

Short Essay. Write a 250-300 word essay to answer four of the following questions.

1. Describe the concept of an ecosystem.
2. Many people think that the human population is immune to the laws of nature. What laws of nature have you studied so far? In your view, can we exempt ourselves? Why or why not? Be specific.
3. Describe what a niche is, and give an example using an organism you are familiar with.
4. Is it best to be a generalist or a specialist in an ecosystem? Support your answer.
5. What ways do humans interfere in the carbon, nitrogen, and phosphorus cycles?
6. Discuss three reasons why biomass decreases the higher you go in most food chains.
7. Give some examples that illustrate the first law of thermodynamics.

Chapter Supplement. The Biomes

Multiple Choice. Each of the following questions has one correct answer. Circle the letter corresponding to the choice you think best answers the question.

B 1. The tundra:

    a. supports coniferous forests.
    b. receives very little precipitation.
    c. is a resilient biome not easily damaged by human activities.
    d. is the year-round home to numerous species of birds.

A 2. Which of the following best describes the taiga?

    a. a biome that extends across North America south of the tundra
    b. dominated by deciduous forests
    c. a region of perpetual ice and snow
    d. a carnivorous forest

D 3. Deciduous trees:

    a. are abundant in the taiga.
    b. cannot survive the tundra because of the warm summers.
    c. have flexible branches that bend under the weight of snow.
    d. act as nutrient pumps.

A 4. Grasslands:

    a. contain plants well adapted to periodic drought.
    b. are found only in temperate climates.
    c. are too cold to support deciduous trees.
    d. have poor soils.

C. 5. Which of the following is an adaptation of most desert and tropical rainforest plants?

    a. succulent water-retaining tissues
    b. wide spacing
    c. shallow root systems
    d. short life spans

Short Essay. Write a 250-300 word essay to answer each of the following questions.

1. Debate the statement: Tropical rainforests should be clearcut to provide additional farmland and pasture to increase food production in many Third World nations.

2. Using your knowledge of evolution, describe the unique conditions of the various biomes and ways they may have influenced the evolution of life forms.

Suggested Readings and Resource Materials

Voigt, John W. (1986). *Everyone's Ecology: Ecological Vignettes* Dubuque, IA: Kendall/Hunt. An interesting collection of essays relating to ecological principles.

These articles, focusing on problems unique to certain ecosystems, are interesting and apply the principles presented in Chapter 3 to different situations.
"Antarctica: Is Any Place Safe From Mankind?" in *Time*, January 15, 1990, pp. 55-62.
"Nature Reserves of the U.S.S.R." in *Sierra*, May/June 1987, pp. 38-45.
"Last Gasp for the Everglades" in *Time*, September 25, 1989, pp. 26-7.

Videos: For ordering information, see Film/Video Index.

Antarctica and *Coastal Dunes* each highlight a particular ecosystem and show the order and form in a seemingly chaotic environment. Contact Films for the Humanities & Sciences.

Life in the Deciduous Forest, The Prairie, and *The Boreal Forest* examine one biome each and describe the interactions between its members. Contact International Film Bureau, Inc.

Niches in the Environment. A filmstrip which examines and illustrates the concepts of niche and ecological succession. Contact International Film Bureau, Inc.

CHAPTER 4

PRINCIPLES OF ECOLOGY:
ECOSYSTEM BALANCE AND IMBALANCE

Outline

I. ECOSYSTEM STABILITY DEFINED

II. WHAT KEEPS ECOSYSTEMS STABLE?
    A. Population Growth and Environmental Resistance
    B. Resisting Change
    C. Species Diversity and Stability

III. CORRECTING IMBALANCE IN ECOSYSTEMS: SUCCESSION
    A. Primary Succession
    B. Secondary Succession

IV. HUMAN IMPACT ON ECOSYSTEMS
    A. Tampering with Biotic Factors
        1. Introducing Competitors
        2. Eliminating or Introducing Predators
        3. Introducing Disease Organisms
    B. Tampering with Abiotic Factors
        1. Pollution
        2. Resource Depletion
    C. Simplifying Ecosystems

V. IMPACT ANALYSIS MODEL
    A. The Impact of Coal Use
        1. Indirect Effects of Human Activities
        2. Direct Effects of Human Activities
    B. Why Study Impacts?
    C. Assessing the Probability of Impacts

VI. RESTORATION ECOLOGY: REESTABLISHING THE BALANCE
    A. Controversy Over Restoration
    B. Benefits of Restoration

VII. CHAPTER SUPPLEMENT. NUCLEAR WAR: PATHWAY TO ENVIRONMENTAL CATASTROPHE

Objectives

After studying this chapter, the student should be able to:

1. Discuss *ecosystem stability* and list factors believed to contribute to *equilibrium*.
2. Define *environmental resistance, inertia*, and *resilience*.
3. Distinguish *primary* and *secondary succession*.
4. Understand the role and limits of *ecological succession* in ecosystem recovery after a disturbance.
5. Discuss the various direct and indirect ways in which humans can have either positive or negative impacts on ecosystems.
6. Use the *impact analysis model* to visualize the interrelatedness of environmental effects from human activities.
7. Identify the goals and methodology of restoration ecology.
8. Characterize the *nuclear winter/fall* hypothesis predictions concerning the environmental effects of nuclear war.

Lecture Notes

I. ECOSYSTEM STABILITY DEFINED
- *Stability* in an ecosystem is a steady state or dynamic equilibrium, where conditions are held more or less constant by *negative feedback systems* operating within the ecosystem.

II. WHAT KEEPS ECOSYSTEMS STABLE?

A. Population Growth and Environmental Resistance
- Ecosystem balance is maintained by the opposing forces of both *biotic* and *abiotic growth* and *reduction factors*.
- *Environmental resistance* is a collective term for those factors which have a negative effect on population growth.

B. Resisting Change
- *Inertia* and *resilience* are characteristics of ecosystems which resist and rapidly recover from change.

C. Species Diversity and Stability
- *Species diversity* and stability seem to be positively correlated for most ecosystems, though *climate uniformity* may also play a major role in ecosystem stability.

III. CORRECTING IMBALANCE IN ECOSYSTEMS: SUCCESSION
- *Succession* is a process whereby one biotic community replaces another.

A. Primary Succession
- The development of a biotic community where none had existed before is *primary succession*.
- Each successional community changes conditions, making them unfavorable for itself and favorable for the next community.
- The final or longest-lasting stage in succession is the *climax*.

28

B. Secondary Succession
  - This takes place when an existing community is disturbed or destroyed, either by natural or human-caused events.
  - *Complexity* and *efficiency* usually increase as ecosystems mature.
  - Species diversity tends to peak in immature, rather than climax, stages.
  - Damage to an ecosystem may be so severe as to essentially prevent recovery by natural succession.

IV. HUMAN IMPACT ON ECOSYSTEMS
  - Humans may alter the biosphere by affecting either biotic or abiotic ecosystem components.

  A. Tampering with Biotic Factors
    1. Introducing Competitors
      - *Alien species* may cause disruption in an ecosystem by *outcompeting* native species.
    2. Eliminating or Introducing Predators
      - *Predators* play a vital role in regulating ecosystem stability. Their elimination, or their introduction into new habitats, can cause serious ecosystem imbalance.
    3. Introducing Disease Organisms
      - Introduced *pathogens* can wipe out native species which are not resistant to the alien disease organism.

  B. Tampering with Abiotic Factors
    1. Pollution
      - Human activities produce *air and water pollution*, which can alter the abiotic environment sufficiently to affect ecosystem balance on local, regional, or global scales.
    2. Resource Depletion
      - *Destruction* or *depletion of resources* for human use can have serious adverse effects on other species.

  C. Simplifying Ecosystems
    - Most human-caused ecosystem changes *simplify* ecosystems by reducing species diversity.
    - Very simple ecosystems, such as *monocultures*, tend to be highly unstable. Their protection often causes other environmental problems.

V. IMPACT ANALYSIS MODEL
  - This model helps us determine the *interrelated environmental impacts* of human activities.

  A. The Impact of Coal Use
    - Air, water, and land are all adversely affected by *coal extraction, transportation*, and *combustion*.
    1. Indirect Effects of Human Activities.
      - By degrading habitat through *pollution*, humans indirectly affect many organisms.
    2. Direct Effects of Human Activities
      - Human activities can directly affect other species and human populations as well.

  B. Why Study Impacts?
    - *Impact models*, though imprecise, can serve as *frameworks* for environmental risk assessment and decision-making.

  C. Assessing the Probability of Impacts
    - Impacts must be assessed both for their *probability* and degree of *(un)desirability*.

VI. RESTORATION ECOLOGY: REESTABLISHING THE BALANCE
- *Restoration ecology* (or *conservation biology*) seeks to restore badly damaged ecosystems.

A. Controversy Over Restoration
- Though sound in principle, restoration can potentially be misused to justify certain development projects which destroy valuable habitat.

B. Benefits of Restoration
- Restoration is economically and aesthetically preferable to other alternatives for slowing or reversing habitat degradation.

VII. CHAPTER SUPPLEMENT. NUCLEAR WAR: PATHWAY TO ENVIRONMENTAL CATASTROPHE

A. The Nuclear Detonation
- Major effects of a nuclear explosion result from intense *heat* and *light*, high *air pressure* and strong *winds, radiation, electromagnetic pulse*, and radioactive *fallout*.

B. Nuclear Winter
- *Nuclear winter/nuclear fall* refer to the dark, cold conditions which many predict will follow any sizeable nuclear exchange.
- Though there are too many variables for us to be able to precisely predict the environmental effects of nuclear war, nearly all agree that the consequences would be severe and long-lasting.

Critical Thinking Problems

1. Suppose that conservation biologists were able to re-create an ecosystem indistinguishable in all respects from one which had been decimated by stripmining. Assuming the engineered one is functionally and aesthetically identical to the original ecosystem, is it as *valuable* as the original? Do origin and authenticity matter when it comes to ecosystems? If not, why do they matter when it comes to art and other valued objects?

Test Questions

Multiple Choice. Each of the following questions has one correct answer. Circle the letter corresponding to the choice you think best answers the question.

C   1. Reducing the number of species in an ecosystem:

     a. generally has no effect on ecosystem stability.
     b. increases the species diversity.
     c. can reduce ecosystem stability.
     d. is called succession.

E   2. A corn field is an example of:

a. a simplified ecosystem.
b. a heteroculture.
c. a monoculture.
d. a diversified ecosystem.
e. a & c
f. b & c

B   3. In an ecosystem, pathogenic organisms:

a. are usually eliminated because they tend to kill off the organisms they infect.
b. are a part of environmental resistance, helping to keep populations in control.
c. can but rarely evolve to counter genetic changes in the organisms they infect.
d. a & b
e. b & c

A   4. The water hyacinth has proliferated in the waters of the southern United States, squeezing out native plants. The water hyacinth is:

a. a competitor.
b. part of a pioneer community.
c. helping to increase species diversity in southern waters.
d. none of the above
e. all of the above

D   5. The sequential replacement of biological communities by new ones:

a. is called primary succession.
b. is called secondary succession.
c. is called environmental resistance.
d. is accelerated if soil has already formed.

D   6. A tropical rain forest is:

a. an example of a simplified unstable ecosystem.
b. a stable ecosystem because of low species diversity.
c. similar to the arctic tundra in terms of its stability.
d. a climax community.

C   7. Favorable weather:

a. is a biotic factor.
b. hinders an organism's biotic potential.
c. is an abiotic growth factor.
d. is a component of environmental resistance.
e. none of the above

A   8. _____ is a characteristic of an ecosystem causing it to "bounce back" from environmental damage.

    a. Resilience
    b. Resistance
    c. Inertia
    d. Instability

F   9. The first community to inhabit a barren region:

    a. is usually not well adapted to the region and quickly replaced.
    b. alters conditions so much that it is eventually replaced.
    c. is called an intermediate community.
    d. is a pioneer community.
    e. a & b
    f. b & d
    g. a & c

C   10. The regrowth of a tropical rain forest where slash-and-burn agriculture is practiced is an example of:

    a. primary succession.
    b. inertia.
    c. secondary succession.
    d. environmental resistance.

Fill in the Blank. For each of the following questions, fill in the blank with the appropriate word or phrase.

1. Fully developed ecosystems are considered to be stable because they remain more or less the same over long periods. This steady state is sometimes called a _____ equilibrium.

2. _____ is the property of an ecosystem that causes it to resist change.

3. _____ _____ is a measure of variety in an ecosystem.

4. _____ _____ is the sum total of all the biotic and abiotic factors that tend to reduce a population's growth.

5. A _____ community is characterized by high species diversity, high stability, and good nutrient conservation.

6. _____ _____ is that branch of biology which seeks to repair and restore badly damaged ecosystems.

Answers: 1. dynamic   2. Inertia   3. Species diversity   4. Environmental resistance   5. climax or mature   6. Restoration ecology

Short Essay. Write a 250-300 word essay to answer each of the following questions.

1. Describe the two major ways humans disrupt ecosystems, and give some examples of each.

2. Using your examples in essay 1, give some ways to prevent disruption and ways to fix mistakes that have already been made.

3. With your knowledge of ecosystems, discuss the balance of nature. In other words, how are ecosystems and populations kept in balance? How are human populations kept in balance?

4. What is secondary succession and how does it differ from primary succession? Give an example of each one.

5. Describe what is meant by ecosystem stability. Why are immature ecosystems less apt to be considered stable?

6. What is ecosystem simplification? Give some examples.

Chapter Supplement. Nuclear War: Pathway to Environmental Catastrophe

Short Essay. Write a 250-300 word essay to answer each of the following questions.

1. Describe each of the following resulting from a nuclear explosion: heat and light, blast winds, direct nuclear radiation, electromagnetic pulse, and fallout. Be sure to discuss how they are produced and their effects.

2. Describe the nuclear winter/fall theory.

Suggested Reading and Resource Materials

Berger, John, Ed. (1989). *Environmental Restoration*. Washington, DC: Island Press. A comprehensive look at current science and strategies for restoring the earth.

Cairns, John, Ed. (1988). *Rehabilitating Damaged Ecosystems*, Vols. I & II. Boca Raton, FL: CRC Press. A broad study of factors involved in rehabilitation project feasibility; includes numerous case studies of actual projects.

Freedman, Bill (1989). *Environmental Ecology*. San Diego: Academic Press. Discusses the impacts of pollution and other stresses on ecosystem structure and function.

McKibben, Bill (1989). *The End of Nature*. New York: Random House. Describes how modern society is changing the earth's atmosphere by slash-and-burn agriculture, fossil fuel combustion, and other practices, and warns of an imminent replacement of "nature" with artificial systems.

Odum, Eugene P. (1989). *Ecology and Our Endangered Life-Support Systems*. Sunderland, MA: Sinauer Associates. Written by the father of modern ecology to provide a citizen's guide to the principles of ecology as they relate to today's environmental threats.

Soulé, Michael E., Ed. (1986). *Conservation Biology*. Sunderland, MA: Sinauer Associates. Diverse array of essays on the effects of various ecosystem disturbances and on ecosystem stability and restoration.

Soulé, M.E. and Kathryn Kohm, Eds. (1989). *Research Priorities for Conservation Biology*. Washington, DC: Island Press. Proposes a research and restoration agenda based on the urgency of various conservation programs.

Videos: For ordering information, see Film/Video Index.

Conservation and Balance in Nature. Critically investigates natural ecosystem balance as it relates to human activities. Contact International Film Bureau, Inc.

Keepers of the Forest. An award-winning video showcasing successful resource management, in tropical rainforests. Contact Umbrella Films.

Nuclear Winter: A Growing Global Concern. Mini-documentary on nuclear winter. Contact The Video Project.

Nuclear Winter: Changing Our Way of Thinking. Carl Sagan presenting his views on this controversial topic. Contact The Video Project.

CHAPTER 5

POPULATION:
MEASURING GROWTH AND ITS IMPACT

Outline

I. DIMENSIONS OF THE POPULATION CRISIS
   A. Too Many People
      1. The Plight of the Cities
      2. Rural Despair
   B. Reproducing Too Quickly

II. THE POPULATION EXPLOSION
   A. The Survival Boom
   B. A Double-Edged Sword: Expansion of the Earth's Carrying Capacity
   C. Exponential Growth

III. UNDERSTANDING POPULATIONS AND POPULATION GROWTH
   A. Measuring Population Growth
      1. Growth Rate
      2. Birth Rates
      3. Death Rates
      4. Fertility and Zero Population Growth
      5. A Comparison of Growth Rates
      6. Doubling Time
   B. Migration
   C. Seeing Is Believing: Population Histograms

IV. THE FUTURE OF WORLD POPULATION: SOME PROJECTIONS

Objectives

After studying this chapter, the student should be able to:

1. Understand and discuss the wide-ranging *environmental*, *social*, *political*, and *economic* implications of human population growth.
2. Cite statistics for the major world and U.S. population parameters: *size*, *growth rates*, and *doubling times*.
3. Define *carrying capacity* and discuss implications for long-term human population support if we exceed this level.
4. Contrast *exponential* and *arithmetic* growth.
5. Draw and interpret *histograms* for expanding, shrinking, and stable populations.
6. Predict the potential effects of *immigration*, *emigration* and *internal migration* on a country's demographics.

Lecture Notes

I. DIMENSIONS OF THE POPULATION CRISIS
- The *population crisis* is responsible for many environmental and social effects seemingly unrelated to growth in human numbers.

A. Too Many People
- As population grows, large cities swell disproportionately.
1. The Plight of the Cities
- *Living standards* deteriorate and *social problems* mushroom under crowded conditions in large cities.
2. Rural Despair
- Overpopulation in rural areas leads to rapid *environmental deterioration, malnutrition, disease,* and *despair.*

B. Reproducing Too Quickly
- Virtually every serious environmental problem today is caused or exacerbated by rapid population growth, especially in *Africa, Asia,* and *Latin America.*

II. THE POPULATION EXPLOSION
- Currently, the world population is *5.3 billion; 90 million* people are added *yearly.*

A. The Survival Boom
- The phenomenal upsurge in population growth in modern times is due to two factors: slightly *increased reproduction* rates and dramatically *decreased death* rates.

B. A Double-Edged Sword: Expansion of the Earth's Carrying Capacity
- Advances in *tools, agriculture, medicine,* and *technology* have increased the earth's *carrying capacity.*
- While necessary to provide for an expanding human population, such increases invariably result in increased *depletion* and *pollution.*

C. Exponential Growth
- Growth at a fixed yearly rate is *exponential.*
- When graphed, exponential growth can be seen to start *slowly,* then round a bend to enter a phase of *increasingly rapid* growth.
- World population is growing *1.8%/year,* doubling in just *40 years.*
- *Resource recovery* and *pollution assimilation* cannot keep up with the rapid growth in human population.

III. UNDERSTANDING POPULATIONS AND POPULATION GROWTH
- *Demography* is the study of population statistics and characteristics.

A. Measuring Population Growth
1. Growth Rate
- *Growth rate* (%) = (Crude Birth Rate - Crude Death Rate) x 100
2. Birth Rates
- *Birth rates* for any population are influenced by *age* of marriage, *educational* level, *contraceptive* use, female *employment,* and couples' *desires, beliefs,* and *values.*

3. Death Rates
   - Rapidly falling *death rates* due to *improved living conditions* and *medical treatment* have caused an increase in growth rate in the past century.
4. Fertility and Zero Population Growth
   - *Total fertility rate (TFR)* is the average number of children a woman will bear.
   - *Replacement-level fertility* is reproduction at exactly that level necessary for couples to replace themselves.
   - Due to *immigration* and momentum from the *lag effect*, most populations will not reach *zero population growth* immediately upon reaching replacement reproduction.
5. A Comparison of Growth Rates
   - Growth rates in *developing* countries on average far exceed those of *developed* nations.
6. Doubling Time
   - $DT = 70/GR(\%)$
   - At current growth rates, world population will *double* in about *40 years*.

B. Migration
   - *Net migration* is immigration minus emigration.
   - *Zero population growth* for any population can only be reached when growth rates and net migration rates are zero.
   - *Intranational* or *internal migration* has had profound demographic, as well as economic and environmental, effects in the U.S.

C. Seeing Is Believing: Population Histograms
   - *Histograms* are graphic representations of the age structure and gender distribution of a population.
   - Shifts in population structure can signal dramatic changes in the economic, employment, infrastructural, and health-care needs of a population.

IV. THE FUTURE OF WORLD POPULATION: SOME PROJECTIONS
   - No finite system can accommodate infinite population growth.
   - Estimates of maximum human population size range from 8 to 15 billion; it may then level off, decrease slowly, or drop dramatically, depending on innumerable variables.

Critical Thinking Problems

1. In Chapter 4, you read about various environmental resistance factors which work to stabilize population size in non-human organisms. When a "natural disaster" such as an earthquake, flood, storm, or disease epidemic befalls a human population, we blame "Mother Nature" or call it "an act of God." Could some of these disasters actually be a consequence of uncontrolled human population growth and the effects of *environmental resistance*? What about increasingly frequent behavior disorders such as drug abuse, violence, and apathy? Could these be forms of environmental resistance? If so, postulate a cause-and-effect relationship.

2. A few thinkers today are warning of a *"birth dearth"* in the U.S., as fertility rates in this country are declining. They warn that we are in danger of losing our culture and values, as growth rates in Communist and Third World nations remain high. However, birth rates have fallen much more among middle and upper class whites than in lower class and minority groups. In what sense, then, can pleas to reverse the decline of birthrates in this country be said to have *racist* and *culturally biased* overtones?

Test Questions

Multiple Choice. Each of the following questions has one correct answer. Circle the letter corresponding to the choice you think best answers the question.

C   1. The number of organisms the biosphere can support indefinitely is called:

     a. the biotic potential.
     b. gross primary productivity.
     c. carrying capacity.
     d. limiting number.

D   2. Which of the following continents is still experiencing an increase in population growth rate?

     a. Asia
     b. Latin America
     c. Europe
     d. Africa

A   3. World population growth:

     a. has rounded the bend of the exponential growth curve.
     b. is now approximately 2.7% per year.
     c. is largely due to growth in developed countries.
     d. is leveling off.

A   4. The developing nations:

     a. generally have high birth rates and relatively low death rates.
     b. have fairly high literacy rates despite poverty.
     c. double in population every 100 years or more.
     d. typically have very low infant mortality because of western medicine.

B   5. The graph showing the percentage of individuals in each age group in a population is called:

     a. an exponential growth curve.
     b. a population histogram.
     c. a sigmoidal growth curve.
     d. an ecological pyramid.

C   6. The total number of children a woman will have in her lifetime if she conforms to the age-specific fertility rates is called the:

     a. general fertility rate.
     b. replacement level fertility.
     c. total fertility rate.
     d. crude birth rate.

D   7. Movement of people within a country, for instance from state to state, is called:

   a. emigration.
   b. immigration.
   c. in-migration.
   d. internal migration.

B   8. The population histogram for Mexico is:

   a. constrictive.
   b. expansive.
   c. mobile.
   d. stationary.

A   9. The increase in world population in the last 100 years is:

   a. due to better control of abiotic and biotic factors, such as famine and disease.
   b. due to a sudden increase in human fertility.
   c. due to an increase in food supplies.
   d. due to an increase in doubling time.

D 10. The increase in life expectancy in the United States in the past 100 years is largely the result of:

   a. improved survival of adults.
   b. lowered suicide rates among teens.
   c. better food.
   d. better medical care of newborns.

Fill in the blank. For each of the following questions, fill in the blank with the appropriate word or phrase.

1. A population growing at 2% per year doubles in _____ years.

2. World population is currently about _____ _____.

3. U.S. population is currently about _____ _____.

4. The movement of people out of a country is called _____.

5. The _____ _____ is the number of children a couple must have to replace themselves.

6. Growth of population by a fixed percentage every year is called _____ growth.

7. The number of births per 100 total population is called the _____ birth rate.

8. _____ _____ _____ occurs when birth rates and death rates are equal and there is no net migration.

9. Seventy divided by the population growth rate is the _____ _____.

10. Sweden's population histogram shows a shrinking base and is defined as a _____ histogram.

Answers: 1. 35   2. 5.3 billion   3. 250 million   4. emigration   5. replacement-level fertility
6. exponential   7. crude   8. Zero population growth   9. doubling time   10. constrictive

Short Essay. Write a 250-300 word essay to answer each of the following questions.

1. The total fertility rate in the United States has been below replacement level for nearly two decades. Why hasn't the United States reached zero population growth?

2. Why has life expectancy increased so dramatically in the United States in the past 70 years?

3. How do humans expand the carrying capacity? How can this be dangerous?

Suggested Readings and Resource Materials

Population/Environment Balance, Inc. publishes a monthly newsletter, "Have You Heard?" which highlights population-related issues and current events. Contact P/E Balance, Washington, DC.

Population Reference Bureau (Annual). *World Population Data Sheet.* Concise and current population statistics.

Repetto, Robert (1987). *Population, Resources, Environment: An Uncertain Future.* Washington, DC: Population Reference Bureau, Inc. Examines the economic and environmental consequences of rapid population growth in poor countries and of incipient decline in rich ones.

Simon, Julian (1981). *The Ultimate Resource.* Princeton, NJ: Princeton Univ. Press. Cornucopian economics by the best-known advocate of population growth.

Wattenberg, Ben J. (1987). *The Birth Dearth.* New York: Pharos Books. The book which got this movement underway.

WorldWatch Paper. "Our Demographically Divided World." Washington, DC: WorldWatch Institute.

Videos: For ordering information, see Film/Video Index.

Population and Pollution. Illustrates relationship between population growth and pollution/depletion. Contact International Film Bureau, Inc.

The Desert Doesn't Bloom Here Anymore. Shows the stress that population expansion is putting on land and other resources. Contact NOVA.

The Silent Explosion. A video narrated by Eric Sevareid and produced by The Population Institute. Contact The Population Institute.

CHAPTER 6

POPULATION CONTROL: KEY TO A SUSTAINABLE SOCIETY

Outline

I. HOW DO WE CONTROL POPULATION GROWTH?
    A. Setting Our Goals
    B. Population Control Strategies
        1. Demographic Transition
        2. Family Planning
        3. Small-Scale Economic Development
    C. Developed Countries -- What Can They Do?
    D. Developing Countries -- What Can They Do?

II. MAKING STRATEGIES WORK
    A. Psychological Barriers
    B. Education Barriers
    C. Religious Barriers
    D. Overcoming the Obstacles

III. ETHICS OF POPULATION CONTROL
    A. Is Reproduction a Personal Right?
    B. Is It Ethical Not to Control Population?

IV. THE STATUS OF POPULATION CONTROL
    A. Encouraging Trends
        1. Developing Nations
        2. Developed Nations
    B. Discouraging Trends

Objectives

After studying this chapter, the student should be able to:

1. Define and discuss the *demographic transition* and related socioeconomic considerations.
2. Identify the roles of *family planning* and *small-scale economic development* in population control.
3. Account for the differences in needs and policies of *developed* and *developing* nations.
4. Discuss the *psychological, educational, religious,* and other *barriers* to population control and suggest ways to circumvent them.
5. Understand and extend the ethical arguments on both sides of the population control debate.
6. Cite instances of successful population control programs and examples of trends which undermine the successes.

Lecture Notes

- In *The Limits To Growth*, evidence presented supports the conclusion that human population growth will be limited by *food shortages* and/or *pollution* in the not-too-distant future.
- Since infinite growth in a finite system is impossible, humans must adopt a sustainable society system by *controlling population growth, recycling, protecting renewable resources,* and *reducing pollution.*

I. HOW DO WE CONTROL POPULATION GROWTH?

    A. Setting Our Goals
- Goals concerning both population *growth* and *size* must be determined.
- There are strong *ecological* and *humanitarian arguments* for *stopping population growth* as soon as possible.

    B. Population Control Strategies
      1. Demographic Transition
- Traditionally, *economic development*, through stimulating the *demographic transition*, was thought the best population control strategy.
- Industrialization will not be the answer, though, where *energy, economic* and *natural resources*, and *time* are limited.

      2. Family Planning
- These programs may be *voluntary, extended voluntary*, or *forced* and aim to provide birth control and motivation for its use to all couples.

      3. Small-Scale Economic Development
- Such initiatives aim to create incentives for women to have fewer children.

    C. Developed Countries -- What Can They Do?
- Though growth in developed countries is comparatively slow, their high level of *affluence* magnifies its environmental effects.

    D. Developing Countries -- What Can They Do?
- Improved funding and implementation of population control programs in developing countries is urgently needed.

II. MAKING STRATEGIES WORK

    A. Psychological Barriers
- Population control efforts must cross the psychological barriers of *security* and *esteem* tied to large family size.

    B. Educational Barriers
- *Less educated* people tend to have more children than do the more highly educated.

    C. Religious Barriers
- *Religious doctrines* continue to foster excess reproduction among those who uncritically accept religious dogma.

    D. Overcoming the Obstacles
- Successful family planning will be compatible with the various *social, educational*, and *religious needs* of the targeted population.

III. ETHICS OF POPULATION CONTROL

A. Is Reproduction a Personal Right?
- Many argue that the *collective rights* of all living humans, and the *integrity* of the *biosphere* which those rights presuppose, supersede individuals' rights to reproduce excessively.

B. Is It Ethical Not to Control Population?
- Ethical *obligations* to *future generations* suggest that it is not morally right to allow population growth today at the expense of tomorrow's citizens.

IV. THE STATUS OF POPULATION CONTROL

A. Encouraging Trends
1. Developing Nations
   - *Developing nations* lack the *resources*, but not the *awareness*, necessary to control population growth.
2. Developed Nations
   - Liberalized *abortion laws*, increased *education* and *employment opportunities* for women, and *changing values* have led to decreased growth rates.

B. Discouraging Trends
- *Aid* to countries wishing to control their population size is paltry compared to world military spending.
- Efforts to increase birth control use have met with little success where simultaneous efforts to address underlying *socioeconomic problems* are not made.

Case Study

Help From the U.N. for Population Control

The world has recognized the need for population control. Hardly a nation is without a population policy. But for many Third World Nations money is a major obstacle to progress in population control.

Today, one of the most important sources of help is the United Nations Fund for Population Activities (UNFPA). Established in the late 1960s with several million dollars from a few donor nations, the organization has seen voluntary pledges increase to over $135 million in 1985 from 100 countries. To date the UNFPA has spent more than $1.3 billion on over 4,500 population and family planning projects in nearly 150 developing countries.

The UNFPA is, to a large extent, responsible for much of the progress in population control in recent decades. It has raised international awareness of population growth through periodic censuses. It has also helped alert the world to the consequences of overpopulation and has helped many governments develop, finance, and carry out population programs. Among international agencies, the UNFPA is noted for its ability to provide money for assistance that has an immediate impact.

Because of a growing concern in many developing nations over population growth, the portion of the UNFPA's budget allocated for family planning services has jumped from 35% to over 50%. In India, Indonesia, Brazil, Nigeria, Bangladesh, and dozens of other countries the agency supports maternal and child health clinics, regional training in contraception, improved contraceptive distribution, and other programs. Its population experts consult with governments on the best ways to control population.

The growing commitment of most developing countries to population control, however, has created a problem in recent years. Requests for UNFPA money have exceeded the supply by about 50%. For the most part, developed countries have responded with an outpouring of generosity. In 1986, the United States, a long-time supporter of the UNFPA, withdrew its backing. The Reagan Administration took this action because of concern for allegedly forced abortions in China, whose family planning programs are supported, in part, by the UNFPA. Fortunately, other countries have increased their share, helping to maintain the organization's budget. Any further reduction in funds will seriously hamper the agency at a time when momentum for population control has peaked. Each year of waiting worsens a problem whose solution is long overdue.

Critical Thinking Problems

1. Few people would deny that free choice concerning reproduction is a basic human right. Are rights absolute, or do they, as the Chinese believe, imply certain responsibilities in their exercise? How might problems of overpopulation modify our conception of "rights" and "responsibilities"?

2. Garrett Hardin states that sharing resources is not the answer to problems of poverty and starvation. Do we have an *obligation* to try to feed as many people as we can, *regardless* of the long-term *consequences* of such actions?

Test Questions

Multiple Choice. Each of the following questions has one correct answer. Circle the letter corresponding to the choice you think best answers the question.

A   1. The overwhelming conclusion of the *Limits to Growth* study was:

   a. without zero population growth, recycling, and control of soil erosion, a stable world system could not be achieved.
   b. population would not crash if the available resource supply were two times larger than we think it is.
   c. exponential population growth is no threat to human society.
   d. continued economic expansion and industrial output are necessary to ensure human survival.

B   2. The government of Singapore uses radio announcements and school programs to promote small family size; this is an example of:

   a. a voluntary family planning program.
   b. an extended voluntary family planning program.
   c. forced family planning.
   d. the demographic transition.

C   3. Which factor was the most important in China's success in controlling population growth?

   a. ration tickets.
   b. posters on clinic walls.
   c. the barefoot doctors.
   d. radio messages.

D   4. Which of the following is true regarding the demographic transition?

    a. Stage 1 is characterized by low birth rates and low death rates.
    b. Rapid population growth is characteristic of stages 1 and 2.
    c. Economic development is the only way to lower death rates and birth rates.
    d. The real danger as far as population growth is concerned is when countries become stuck in Stage 2.

C   5. Approximately _____ of the world's population lives in extreme poverty without adequate housing and without enough to eat.

    a. one half
    b. three fourths
    c. one fifth
    d. three fifths

Fill in the blank. For each of the following questions, fill in the blank with the appropriate word or phrase.

1. A _____ is any device, method, or chemical that prevents fertilization.

2. _____ programs are those that make contraceptives available to the public and involve no pressure from the government.

3. _____ allows couples to determine the number and spacing of their offspring.

4. Labor-intensive industry that uses local resources to meet local needs is called _____ technology.

5. _____ percent of the world's population is under the age of 15.

Answers: 1. contraceptive   2. Voluntary   3. Family planning   4. appropriate   5. 35

Short Essay. Write a 250-300 word essay to answer each of the following questions.

1. Why are many countries stuck in stage 2 of the demographic transition? Why is this so dangerous?

2. Briefly describe how education affects the birth rate.

3. Describe the major reasons why birth control in India has proved to be a failure.

4. Describe the major strategies you would recommend for population control in the developing world; do the same for the developed world.

Readings and Resource Materials

Bales, M. D. (1980). "Famine or Food: Sacrificing for Future or Present Generations." In *Responsibilities To Future Generations* by Ernest Partridge, New York: Prometheus Books. A stimulating article examining Garrett Hardin's "lifeboat ethics" and the ethics of population control in general.

Brown, Lester (1978). *The Twenty-Ninth Day*. Washington, DC: WorldWatch Institute. Classic book on the need to control population growth.

Jacobson, Jodi (1989). "The Baby Budget." WorldWatch, Sept/Oct 1989, pp. 21-40. Thorough examination of China's one-child family program and how modernization is putting it to the test.

WorldWatch Paper. "Population Policies for a New Economic Era." Contact WorldWatch Institute, Washington, DC.

WorldWatch Paper. "Promoting Population Stabilization: Incentives for Small Families." Contact WorldWatch Institute, Washington, DC.

CHAPTER 7

FEEDING THE WORLD'S PEOPLE:
FOOD AND AGRICULTURE

Outline

I. THE DIMENSIONS OF HUNGER
  A. Diseases of Malnutrition
    1. Kwashiorkor
    2. Marasmus
    3. Effects of Severe Malnutrition
  B. Declining Food Supplies
  C. Long-Term Challenges

II. PROBLEMS FACING WORLD AGRICULTURE
  A. Soil Erosion
  B. Desertification: Turning Cropland to Desert
  C. Depletion of Soil Nutrients
  D. High Energy Costs and Diminishing Supplies
  E. Water Mismanagement
    1. Agricultural Groundwater Depletion
    2. Competition for Water
    3. Waterlogging and Salinization
  F. Conversion to Nonagricultural Uses
  G. Conversion of Cropland to Fuel Farms: A Future Problem
  H. Politics and World Hunger
  I. Loss of Genetic Diversity

III. BUILDING A SUSTAINABLE AGRICULTURAL SYSTEM
  A. Increasing the Amount of Agricultural Land
    1. Exploiting Farmland Reserves
    2. Reducing the Spread of Deserts
    3. Soil Conservation
    4. Other Protective Measures
  B. Increasing the Yield of Cropland
    1. Preserving Genetic Diversity
    2. New Plant and Animal Varieties
    3. Soil Enrichment Programs
    4. Improving Irrigation Efficiency
  C. New Foods and Food Supplements
    1. Native Species
    2. Fish From the Sea
    3. Commercial Fish Farms: Mariculture and Aquaculture
    4. Eating Lower on the Food Chain
  D. Reducing Pest Damage and Spoilage
  E. Increasing Self-Sufficiency

F.   Political and Economic Solutions
G.   An Integrated Approach

IV.   CHAPTER SUPPLEMENT. THE PROMISES AND PERILS OF GENETIC ENGINEERING
A.   The Promises
B.   The Risk Debate

Objectives

After studying this chapter, the student should be able to:
1.   Appreciate the *dimensions* of world hunger and the manifestations of malnutrition.
2.   List and discuss the *environmental repercussions* of efforts to expand world food supplies.
3.   Characterize a *sustainable agricultural system* suitable for Third World or developed nations.
4.   Identify several ways by which food supplies could potentially be expanded without causing environmental damage.
5.   Understand the role of *population growth* in exacerbating worldwide food shortages.
6.   Discuss *soil formation, characterization,* and *management.*
7.   Debate the pros and cons of *genetic engineering* as a way to expand food supplies and address world hunger.

Lecture Notes

I.   THE DIMENSIONS OF HUNGER
   •   *Hunger* is widespread; it is especially prevalent in Asia, Africa, and Latin America.

   A.   Diseases of Malnutrition
      •   *40 million* people die yearly from malnutrition-related disease.
      1. Kwashiorkor
         •   Protein-deficiency disease, or *kwashiorkor,* strikes children soon after weaning.
      2. Marasmus
         •   Protein- and calorie-deficiency produce *marasmus.*
         •   Less obvious effects of moderate malnutrition include *decreased immunity.*
      3. Effects of Severe Malnutrition
         •   *Severe malnutrition* produces serious and permanent mental and physical impairment.

   B.   Declining Food Supplies
      •   Recent droughts have caused food surpluses to dwindle; poor nations are increasingly and precariously dependent on imports to avoid famine.

   C.   Long-Term Challenges
      •   A *sustainable system* of *agriculture* is needed to meet the present and future needs for food and to protect soil and water.

II.   PROBLEMS FACING WORLD AGRICULTURE
   •   In both poor and rich nations, incentives work to encourage farmers to ignore sustainable agriculture practices.

   A.   Soil Erosion
      •   This is the most *serious* agricultural problem today.

48

- *Erosion* not only destroys productivity but contributes heavily to air and water pollution problems.

B. Desertification: Turning Cropland to Desert
- Mistreatment of soils in arid regions leads to *desertification*.
- Previous civilizations have caused desertification; today, the problem is widespread, but particularly bad in Africa.

C. Depletion of Soil Nutrients
- Modern farming practices *deplete soil nutrients*; their replacement with artificial fertilizers causes serious environmental problems.

D. High Energy Costs and Diminishing Supplies
- Food production today relies heavily on *fossil fuel* consumption; as fuel supplies dwindle, food prices will rise correspondingly.
- Approximately 9 calories of fuel are consumed for every 1 calorie of food produced; this imbalance is clearly *unsustainable*.

E. Water Mismanagement
- *Irrigation* supports world food production to a large extent.
1. Agricultural Groundwater Depletion
   - *Groundwater*, stored in *aquifers*, is being withdrawn faster than it can be replaced.
2. Competition for Water
   - Various sectors inside and outside of agriculture *compete* with food producers for irrigation water.
3. Waterlogging and Salinization
   - On poorly drained irrigated lands, *waterlogging* and *salinization* can reduce yields and damage soils.

F. Conversion to Nonagricultural Uses
- Farmland is lost as urbanization, energy production, transportation, and other forms of development take land out of agricultural production.

G. Conversion of Cropland to Fuel Farms: A Future Problem
- *Bio-fuel* production involves a necessary conflict: food for people versus fuel for cars.

H. Politics and World Hunger
- *Political decisions* and *government policies* can discourage the efficient production and distribution of food and the good husbandry of soils.

I. Loss of Genetic Diversity
- New varieties of crops, such as those introduced in the *Green Revolution*, have substantially *increased yields* but *decreased genetic diversity* of crop plants; this increases *vulnerability* to pests, disease organisms, and environmental stress.

III. BUILDING A SUSTAINABLE AGRICULTURAL SYSTEM
- *Population growth* and *food shortages* both contribute to worldwide hunger and starvation.

A. Increasing the Amount of Agricultural Land
1. Exploiting Farmland Reserves

- In those areas of the world with uncultivated potential farmlands, a major expansion of *cultivation* would have severe *undesirable ecological effects*, such as wildlife habitat depletion.

2. Reducing the Spread of Deserts
   - On land currently in cultivation or damaged by other activities, *topsoil protection* and *revegetation* to halt deforestation must take priority.

3. Soil Conservation
   - Government policies and financial incentives can encourage *topsoil conservation* in both developed and developing nations.

4. Other Protective Measures
   - Measures designed to stop the conversion or development of good farmland are urgently needed.

B. Increasing the Yield of Cropland
   1. Preserving Genetic Diversity
      - The larger the crop-plant gene pools we maintain, the more yield-increasing *genetic boosts* we can hope to give our crops.
   2. New Plant and Animal Varieties
      - Plant- and animal-breeders may create *new varieties* which maintain or increase yield while maximizing efficiency and minimizing environmental drawbacks.
      - *Genetic engineering* may contribute substantially to increased yields, but serious risks and problems remain to be resolved.
   3. Soil Enrichment Programs
      - These aim to maintain or increase *soil fertility*.
   4. Improving Irrigation Efficiency
      - New delivery systems can dramatically reduce the water needed to irrigate a given field.

C. New Foods and Food Supplements
   - Because of cost, energy inefficiency, and consumer resistance, highly *unconventional new food sources* will not feed the world's hungry.
   1. Native Species
      - Numerous *native plant* and *animal species* have potential to efficiently expand our food supply.
   2. Fish From the Sea
      - Most commercial marine species are threatened today by *overharvesting* and *pollution*.
      - Improved yields are not likely to come from increased catch but rather *reduced spoilage* during handling and processing.
   3. Commercial Fish Farms: Mariculture and Aquaculture
      - Low-input *mariculture* and *aquaculture* could substantially increase protein supplies in poor nations.
   4. Eating Lower on the Food Chain
      - While theoretically appealing, this approach has limited practical applicability in the developed nations, though it can serve as a useful rule of thumb in developing countries.

D. Reducing Pest Damage and Spoilage
   - Affordable, environmentally sound techniques exist for controlling *crop damage* and *food spoilage*; widespread implementation could increase food supplies 10% or more.

E. Increasing Self-Sufficiency
- *Self-sufficiency* is increasingly desirable today for developing nations.
- This is enhanced by aid and assistance aimed at building a *sustainable agricultural system* appropriate for a particular culture.

F. Political and Economic Solutions
- Thoughtful changes in *government policies* and *economic incentives* could increase agricultural efficiency and reduce resource depletion and pollution.

G. An Integrated Approach
- There is no one solution to the problems of world hunger and soil depletion; rather, the answer will be a variety of ideas and approaches *integrated* into a policy fostering long-term *sustainable* agricultural production.

IV. CHAPTER SUPPLEMENT. SOIL AND SOIL MANAGEMENT

A. What Is Soil?
- *Soils* are mixtures of *organic* and *inorganic materials* varying in a number of features.
- A variety of physical processes and organisms' activities contribute to *soil formation* from *parent material*.
- Soils have layers, or *horizons*, which differ in type and thickness between different soil types.
- *Climate, geological features, biotic factors,* and *age* determine a given region's *soil profile*.

B. Soil Management
- Soil is managed to *control erosion* and *preserve nutrients*.
- *Erosion control* can be achieved through *minimum tillage, contour farming, strip cropping, terracing, gully reclamation,* and *shelterbelts*.
- *Nutrient preservation* is enhanced by *use of organic* or *synthetic fertilizers* and *crop rotation*.
- In *organic farming*, the use of synthetic inputs, and thus environmental impact, is minimized; *sustainability* is achieved.

C. Achieving Cost-Effective Conservation
- A variety of new *regulations, incentives,* and *programs* aimed at low-cost *topsoil conservation* would be effective.

V. CHAPTER SUPPLEMENT. THE PROMISES AND PERILS OF GENETIC ENGINEERING

A. The Promises
- *Genetic engineering* may increase food supplies by *protecting* crops from pests, diseases, or environmental damage and by allowing crops to thrive in damaged or depleted soils.

B. The Risk Debate
- Since genetically altered organisms may pose risks similar to those posed by alien species, *caution* and *further study* are called for concerning their use.

Critical Thinking Problems

1. *Genetic engineering* appeals to our desire to find a technological fix for the problems of agriculture and world hunger eradication. Suppose we can incorporate genes for salt-tolerance and nitrogen fixation into grain crops. Might this be detrimental in the long run by removing our incentives to practice good soil husbandry? Or will there always be a technological solution even for the problems caused by previous technological fixes?

2. Does every human have a *right* to a nutritionally sufficient diet? If so, are we in the developed world morally obligated to give up meat and automobiles in order to make resources available to fight world hunger? If not, defend your position.

Test Questions

Multiple Choice. Each of the following questions has one correct answer. Circle the letter corresponding to the choice you think best answers the question.

F   1.   Kwashiorkor:

   a.   is characterized by edema (fluid accumulation).
   b.   is a disease common in newly weaned children.
   c.   results from an insufficient intake of protein and calories.
   d.   is caused primarily by protein deficiency.
   e.   a & c
   f.   b & d

A   2.   Marasmus:

   a.   is characterized by wasting of the limbs and diarrhea.
   b.   is most common in the developed countries.
   c.   results from a vitamin A deficiency in infants.
   d.   usually occurs in children past the age of 5.

C   3.   Soil erosion:

   a.   is primarily a problem in developing countries.
   b.   is determined primarily by the slope of the land.
   c.   depletes soil of nutrients and can lower productivity.
   d.   exceeds replacement on nearly 75% of American farmland.

B   4.   Which of the following is true regarding the Green Revolution?

   a.   It began in the 1970s in the United States.
   b.   Its primary purpose was to increase grain output per acre.
   c.   It relied heavily on genetic engineering to produce new high-yield varieties.
   d.   It produced high-yield, insect- and disease-resistant crops.

D   5.   Expanding world food production:

a. can be best brought about by developing new foods.
b. will be the primary responsibility of the United States because we have the largest reserve of unused (potential) farmland.
c. can be brought about in the United States in all major agricultural regions by increasing the use of groundwater.
d. requires an integrated plan involving an increase in cropland, control of erosion and desertification, expansion of irrigation, and development of new plant varieties.

C.   6.   Native grazers:

a. are an inferior source of meat.
b. convert a lower percentage of plant biomass to animal biomass than conventional grazers (cattle).
c. provide many benefits, especially disease resistance.
d. generally do more damage to native vegetation than domestic varieties.

D   7.   A worldwide sustainable agricultural system:

a. would be best implemented by exporting modern technologies to the developing nations.
b. would probably require large inputs of artificial fertilizer to sustain growth.
c. could be built by simply continuing what we are doing now throughout the world.
d. requires strict soil erosion control, control of grazing, and replenishment of soil using organic fertilizers.

A   8.   Which of the following does not increase the rate of soil erosion from rain water?

a. planting grasses and alfalfa for pasture
b. planting corn and other row crops
c. plowing soil
d. urban development, sidewalks, roadways, and so on

E   9.   Genetic diversity in agriculture:

a. is decreased as we wipe out valuable wild relatives of crops we now depend on for food.
b. is not much of a problem because we only depend on a few species of plants and animals for our food.
c. is decreased as we rely on a smaller number of plants and animals for food production.
d. is a problem only in the developing nations.
e. a & c
f. b & d

B   10.   Fuel farms:

    a. will probably not affect world food prices.
    b. grow crops that can be converted to alcohol and other fuels.
    c. could easily provide substitutes for all of our liquid fuels.
    d. will probably not affect world food supplies.

C   11.   Desertification:

    a. is only a problem in the developing nations.
    b. is always the result of drought.
    c. results from overgrazing and poor land management in arid regions.
    d. is a new problem cropping up only in the last 50 years.

Fill in the Blank. For each of the following questions, fill in the blank with the appropriate word or phrase.

1. Zones of porous materials, such as sandstone, which are saturated with water are called _____.

2. The build up of calcium carbonate and other minerals from irrigation waters is called _____.

3. The destruction of farmland by urban sprawl is called _____ _____.

4. _____ is the production of edible fish in salty or brackish water.

5. A lack of the proper nutrients in the human diet is called _____.

6. The _____ _____ zone is the region where rain water and snow melt replenish groundwater.

7. _____ is a problem characterized by a rise of the water table and the death of crops and is caused by over-irrigation of land.

8. One of the chief fuels produced on fuel farms is _____.

9. The U.S. law that authorized huge surplus grain shipments from the U.S. to Third World nations is called the _____ _____ _____ Act.

10. _____ _____ was awarded the Nobel Prize for his work on improving crop yield.

Answers: 1. aquifers   2. salinization   3. farmland conversion   4. Mariculture   5. malnutrition
6. aquifer recharge   7. Waterlogging   8. alcohol (ethanol)   9. Farm Surplus Disposal   10. Norman Borlaug

Short Essay. Write a 250-300 word essay to answer each of the following questions.

1. List the major problems facing world agriculture today. Which one(s) is (are) the most significant?

2. What is genetic engineering and how can it be used to increase agricultural output?

3. Defend or refute the following statement: "The Green Revolution has been a complete failure."

4. Discuss the major ways to increase world food output.

5. How do the supply and demand of fossil fuel energy affect world agriculture?

Chapter Supplement. Soil and Soil Management

Multiple Choice. Each of the following questions has one correct answer. Circle the letter corresponding to the choice you think best answers the question.

B   1.   Soil:

         a. is composed mostly of organic matter from rotted plants.
         b. is divided into four more or less distinct layers.
         c. forms from hard rock in 50 years or less.
         d. is rarely affected by biological organisms.
         e. a & b
         f. c & d

E   2.   Minimum tillage:

         a. saves fuel and reduces erosion.
         b. reduces soil moisture loss.
         c. may increase some insect populations.
         d. usually requires more herbicide application to control weeds.
         e. all of the above
         f. none of the above

A   3.   Strip cropping:

         a. is the planting of alternate crops to reduce soil erosion.
         b. involves planting crops along lines that follow the contour of the field.
         c. is only practiced on hilly terrain.
         d. involves the planting of rows of trees along the edges of fields to protect them from the wind.

B   4.   Organic fertilizers:

         a. are poor soil supplements because they do not add the necessary nutrients to soil.
         b. are useful because organic materials increase soil water retention.
         c. are not recommended because they change soil acidity.
         d. tend to increase water pollution.

D   5.   Organic farms:

      a.   produce less food per acre at a higher cost than conventional farms.
      b.   produce more food per acre but at a lower cost than conventional farms.
      c.   require no input of inorganic fertilizer.
      d.   emphasize conservation of soil and the use of organic fertilizers whenever possible.

Fill in the Blank. For each of the following questions, fill in the blank with the appropriate word or phrase.

1.   Erosion on hilly terrain can be blocked or slowed down by building _____, earthen berms that cut across the fall line of the hill.

2.   The _____ horizon is the productive layer of soil.

3.   A row of trees planted along the edges of farm fields to reduce soil erosion by wind is called a _____.

4.   Farmers who alternate crops in their fields are practicing _____ _____.

5.   The _____ _____ is the layer from which soil is originally made.

Answers: 1. terraces   2. A   3. shelterbelt   4. crop rotation   5. D horizon (parent material)

Short Essay. Write a 250-300 word essay to answer each of the following questions.

1.   Describe several effective ways that soil conservation can be improved in this country and in Third World nations.

2.   List and describe the pros and cons of organic farming.

3.   Discuss the ways that animals contribute to soil formation.

Suggested Readings and Resource Materials

American Farmland Trust works to safeguard farmland, influence farm-related legislation, and encourage the adoption of sustainable farming practices. For literature and information, contact them at 1717 Massachusetts Ave., N.W., Washington, DC 20036.

The *Amicus Journal* Fall 1989 issue contains two good articles on the environmental effects of modern agriculture: "The Kesterson Syndrome" by Tom Harris (pp. 4-9) and "Kicking the Pesticide Habit" by Kitty Mattes (pp. 10-17).

Dover, Michael and Lee Talbot (1987). *To Feed the Earth: Agro-Ecology for Sustainable Development.* Washington: World Resources Institute. Looks at sustainable agriculture, focusing on Third World issues.

Fox, Michael W. (1986). *Agricide: The Hidden Crisis That Affects Us All.* New York: Schocken Books. An in-depth critique of the modern livestock industry and the impacts of our meat-laden diets.

Peters, William and Lem Neuenschwander (1988). *Slash and Burn: Farming in the Third World Forest.* Univ. of Idaho Press. Penetrating, thoughtful study of forest agriculture in the tropics.

Sampson, R. Neil (1988). "United States Agriculture: Bankruptcy Midst Abundance." In *Orion*, Spring 1988, pp. 13-21.

WorldWatch Institute publishes several papers pertaining to agriculture, including: "U.S. and Soviet Agriculture: The Shifting Balance of Power" by Lester Brown, "Beyond the Green Revolution: New Approaches for Third World Agriculture" by Edward C. Wolf, "The Changing World Food Prospect: The Nineties and Beyond" by Lester Brown, and "Soil Erosion: Quiet Crisis in the World Economy" by Brown and Wolf.

Videos: For ordering information, see Film/Video Index.

Common Ground: Farming and Wildlife. A National Audubon Society special which shows how farming can be both profitable for farmers and good for wildlife. Contact Audubon Television Programs.

Seeds Of Tomorrow. Examines agriculture's genetic heritage and efforts worldwide to protect this heritage for future use. Contact NOVA.

Will The World Starve? NOVA examines damage done by Green Revolution attempts to expand agricultural production. Contact NOVA.

CHAPTER 8

WILDLIFE AND PLANTS:
PRESERVING BIOLOGICAL DIVERSITY

Outline

I. THE VANISHING SPECIES

II. WHAT CAUSES EXTINCTION?
   A. Alteration of Habitat
   B. Commercial, Sport, and Subsistence Hunting
   C. Introducing Foreign Species
   D. Pest and Predator Control
   E. Collecting for Zoos, Individuals, and Research
   F. Pollution
   G. Ecological Factors That Contribute to Extinction
   H. Keystone Species

III. WHY SAVE ENDANGERED SPECIES?
   A. Aesthetics
   B. Ethics
   C. Economics
   D. Ecosystem Stability
   E. Opposing Views

IV. HOW CAN WE SAVE ENDANGERED SPECIES?
   A. Technical Solutions
      1. Integrated Species Management
      2. Zoos Lend a Hand
      3. Helping Third World Nations Protect Priority Areas
      4. Beyond Habitat Protection: Germ Plasm Repositories
   B. Legal Solutions
   C. Personal Solutions

V. WILDLIFE REPORT

Objectives

After studying this chapter, the student should be able to:

1. Discuss the *implications* of human-accelerated versus natural extinction.
2. List the major *causes* of extinction today and rank them in order of relative importance.
3. Give the major arguments in favor of attempting to save all endangered species.
4. Evaluate and critique the major arguments *opposed* to species protection at the expense of economic development.
5. Outline a comprehensive program to protect *global biodiversity*.

58

6. Identify the role of the individual in species protection.
7. Characterize the current state of wildlife protection in the U.S. and worldwide.

Lecture Notes

I. THE VANISHING SPECIES
- *Extinction* is a natural process, but our activities have accelerated the rate of species extinction to levels which are neither natural nor desirable.

II. WHAT CAUSES EXTINCTION?

   A. Alteration of Habitat
- *Habitat alteration/destruction* is the primary cause of species extinction today.
- *Tropical rainforests* comprise the most rapidly disappearing habitat; other threatened, critical habitats include *coral reefs, wetlands,* and *estuaries.*

   B. Commercial, Sport, and Subsistence Hunting
- *Hunting* for *profit, food,* or *sport* threatens certain species which are commercially or otherwise valuable.

   C. Introducing Foreign Species
- *Alien species* can harm native species through the direct effects of *competition* and through indirect effects.

   D. Pest and Predator Control
- *Pesticides* can harm many non-target species.
- Some species of *predators* have been seriously damaged by misguided eradication efforts aimed at protecting livestock.

   E. Collecting for Zoos, Individuals, and Research
- Collecting animals to serve as *zoo* or *research specimens* or as *pets* depletes wild populations; trade in wild plants and plant parts has decimated many populations of certain species, especially the *cacti* and *insectivorous plants.*

   F. Pollution
- A wide variety of *pollutants* threaten wildlife directly and make them more susceptible to disease and environmental stress.
- Sources include *agricultural runoff/drainage, acid rain, oil spills, lead shot,* and *industrial toxins* such as PCB's.

   G. Ecological Factors That Contribute to Extinction
- Certain traits make some species especially *vulnerable* to extinction. These include a *high critical population size, specialization, narrow range, large size,* and *intolerance* of human presence.

   H. Keystone Species
- *Keystone species,* though often inconspicuous or obscure, play a critical role in maintaining ecosystem balance and integrity. Their protection is particularly important.

III. WHY SAVE ENDANGERED SPECIES?

  A. Aesthetics
     • Each species has some *aesthetic value*; every extinction diminishes the aesthetic quality of human life.

  B. Ethics
     • If, as some thinkers believe, every species has a right to exist, then humans have an *ethical obligation* to respect that right.

  C. Economics
     • A large number of species do or potentially might contribute to human utility; that is, they *directly* or *indirectly benefit* us *economically*.

  D. Ecosystem Stability
     • *Ecosystem stability* is enhanced by *species diversity*. Decreased biodiversity threatens ecosystem, and thus human, survival.

  E. Opposing Views
     • Some argue that the loss of any one species is insignificant; however, the cumulative loss of many "insignificant" species is indeed significant, and can only be prevented by protecting as many species as possible.

IV. HOW CAN WE SAVE ENDANGERED SPECIES?

  A. Technical Solutions
     1. Integrated Species Management
        • This approach consists of a wide array of techniques for *protecting habitat* and *reducing human impact* on wildlife.
     2. Zoos Lend a Hand
        • Zoo-sponsored *captive breeding programs* may help save a few critically endangered species.
     3. Helping Third World Nations Protect Priority Areas
        • Developed nations must provide funding to establish and maintain *bio-reserves* in impoverished nations.
        • *Extractive reserves* provide both protection for species and income for humans through sustainable harvesting.
     4. Beyond Habitat Protection: Germ Plasm Repositories
        • Seeds and other plant parts stored in *genetic repositories* preserve germ plasm of species which might otherwise become extinct.

  B. Legal Solutions
     • The *Endangered Species Act* is the major legal instrument for species preservation in the U.S.
     • Worldwide, *weak laws* and *inadequate enforcement* make species protection more difficult.

  C. Personal Solutions
     • Opportunities for personal involvement in species protection range from *enlightened consumerism* to volunteer *activism*.

V. WILDLIFE REPORT

- While many efforts to protect endangered wildlife have been successful, a growing number of species are threatened by *human activities* and *habitat disturbance*.

Case Studies

Controversy Over Grizzlies in Montana

The Grizzly is an animal that has suffered tremendously under human influence. At one time an estimated 1 million grizzlies, maybe more, roamed the lower 48. It ranged from Mexico to Alaska, and east all the way into Minnesota. As the west became settled, however, the grizzlies were forced into mountainous terrain, but even there they were not protected. Like other predators, they were relentlessly trapped and hunted. Only in Montana's vast wilderness and only because of Montana's progressive hunting laws, which were passed in the first half of the 1900's, did the grizzly survive. Today, however, there are only 800 or so in remote pockets of Montana and Wyoming. In Canada and Alaska, grizzly populations are still quite large, but overhunting and development could some day threaten them as well.

Thanks to protection, the U.S. grizzly population may have stabilized, even increased. Now, the Montana Department of Fish, Wildlife, and Parks wants the grizzlies in the northern part of the state in and around Glacier National Park to be taken off the federal list of threatened species. They claim that the bear no longer needs this protection.

The National Wildlife Federation and other wildlife advocates argue that the grizzly should not be "de-listed" until scientists unanimously agree that it and its habitats are out of danger. Opponents of de-listing the bear think that the state's estimates of grizzly populations are in error. The argument boils down to a very simple matter: State biologists believe that there are more than 650 grizzlies in Montana, which they say is more than enough to warrant de-listing. Critics argue that far too little is known about bear populations to warrant such actions.

Estimates of grizzly bear population sizes are not easy to come by. Grizzlies inhabit incredibly rugged terrain with no roads and few trails. The bears themselves are nocturnal, reclusive, and range over wide areas. Estimating population sizes is extraordinarily difficult.

The controversy over protecting grizzlies often becomes acrimonious. To ranchers, the bear is an indiscriminate killer of people and livestock. It threatens their livelihood and their lives, they say. To others, the grizzly is a symbol of American wilderness. They say the bear and the wilderness must be dealt with on their own terms, which is one of the major attractions of wilderness.

The push for de-listing the bear comes from increasing reports of human-grizzly conflict. Some say that's because the bear population has increased. Montana wildlife officials believe that, because grizzlies are found more and more in the plains these days, the bear population has exceeded the capacity of the mountain habitat. Sub-adult bears, they think, must establish their new territories and therefore move out of the mountains onto ranch lands where they have been absent for decades. They are calling for measures (once again) to control the grizzly population.

To prevent conflicts, the state has hired a full-time grizzly control specialist who darts troublesome grizzlies and removes them from areas where they come into conflict with humans. But moving a grizzly is expensive; it costs more than $1,000 per bear.

Relocation of grizzlies, say Montana officials, is hindered by federal protection under the Endangered Species Act (Chapter 8). In order for a state official to get action, he or she must first contact federal officials for permission. It may take several days for an answer, which impairs efforts to reduce conflicts. Because of this, the state is eager to take over bear management. In order for this to happen, though, they argue that the bear must be de-listed; that is, taken off the list of threatened species.

In 1982 state and federal agencies said that the bear would be officially recovered when its Montana population reached 560, and when 56 females had cubs. State biologists believe that the current population in Montana ranges from 549 to 813 and that at least 60 females have cubs. Montana officials argue that the whole purpose of the Endangered Species Act is to get a species to recover, and then to take it off the list. But critics think that it may be too soon.

Environmentalists point out that the state does have power to manage the bear and doesn't need more. The state, for example, does have a grizzly-hunting season (in some parts of the state) and has authority to remove troublesome bears and destroy them.

To help bring the controversy to an end, state and federal biologists are now discussing their differences. Biologists hope to make more accurate determinations of population size. Charles Jonkel, a University of Montana grizzly expert who has been studying the bear for nearly three decades, argues that the grizzly should not be de-listed. The Endangered Species Act, he says, provides money for the protection of the bears. Under state control, the bear would then fall under the purview of the state legislature, which is controlled largely by ranchers. They are unlikely to be sympathetic to this species, whose future hangs in the balance.

Adapted from: Robins, J. (1988). Grizzly and Man: When Species Collide. *National Wildlife*, 26(2): 20-27.

Controversy Over Wild Boars

Wild boars are the center of a raging controversy between environmentalists, park rangers, foresters, and hunters in North Carolina. In 1912, 60 boars escaped from a private hunting preserve in North Carolina. Imported from Europe a decade earlier, the boars thrived in the outlying areas, breeding with domestic pigs and among themselves. Today, they have spread into most of the forests of North Carolina.

Trouble began in the late 1940s when the boar moved into the Great Smoky Mountains National Park. In 1977, President Jimmy Carter signed a proclamation calling on the Park Service to eradicate the boar from the parklands. Why?

Opponents of the boar worry that hogs could carry disease that might spread to humans and domestic swine. More importantly, boars damage the environment. Perhaps the most notable damage is wrought by rooting. Hogs upend enormous amounts of soil in search of food. They are especially fond of the starchy underground roots or tubers where plants hold their nutrients over the winter. Biologists have reported entire fields of wild flowers that have been uprooted by the hungry hogs.

Boars eat almost anything above or below the ground. Their diet includes snails, snakes, small animals, insects, eggs and carrion. They have even been known to prey on fawns, birds, and rare salamanders. Park officials worry that they are destroying the ecological fabric of the park.

Their favorite food is dried fruit, which biologists call mast. The hard fruit of trees is also a favorite food source of deer, bear, turkeys, and other species. The more the hogs eat, the less there is for the other species to survive, say critics, especially during the harsh winters.

Although the hogs are environmentally destructive and displace numerous native species, hunters and many local businesses are struggling to protect the animal. Boar hunting brings considerable revenue to western North Carolina. In fact, restaurants, grocery stores, and sporting goods stores do a record business around boar season.

Today, the park service uses local volunteers to help trap the hogs in the national park and transport them to the Nantahala National Forest, where the boar is hunted in the fall. Unpaid volunteers work 7 days a week trapping boars, from March until November. The transplant program, however, has environmentalists up in arms for fear that the damage is being shifted elsewhere.

Unfortunately, no one knows whether the hog-control program is working. Their high reproductive potential allows their populations to bounce back rapidly. Thus, even though large numbers are taken from the park each year, biologists fear that the populations may spring back almost immediately. A sow can farrow twice a year, producing 4-10 piglets in each litter, frustrating the efforts of government officials.

Wild boars are also causing problems in Hawaii and much of California. In 1923, about two dozen European wild boars were shipped from North Carolina to Monterey County, California. Unfortunately, the imports broke out of their pens and have been spreading throughout the countryside, breeding freely with domestic pigs. Wild boars have been spotted in about half of California's 58 counties. Experts believe that their numbers are still on the rise. In their new home, boars can cause much greater damage because the soils are thin and easily erodible in many areas.

In Hawaii, wild boars were also introduced by humans and have caused enormous problems because of high rainfall, steep slopes, and thin soils. Hawaii has no native grazing mammals and therefore plants are poorly adapted to grazers, especially those like the boar with insatiable appetites. The boars not only destroy vegetation, but also eat the food sources of other native species. For instance, one species of Hawaiian honeycreeper was discovered only 15 years ago. The bird lives in the forest and feeds on snails only in a small section on the north slope of Maui's Haleakala volcano. Wild boars invaded the region in 1970 and have stripped much of the vegetation and eaten much of the food for this bird. Not surprising, the bird is now listed as an endangered species.

The Great Smoky Mountains National Park spends $200,000 per year to remove hogs from the park. No one knows the full extent of the ecological damage they have caused in North Carolina, California and Hawaii, but one thing is certain: The boar will be with us forever, wreaking havoc long after its careless introduction to a strange new land.

Adapted from: Schwartz, D. (1988). Hog Havoc. *National Wildlife*, 26 (4), pp. 14-17.

Critical Thinking Problems

1. Everyone recognizes that, in order to survive, humans must alter their environment and affect other species. However, we also grant other species' claims to exist without unnecessary disturbance by humans. Is there a way to distinguish important from trivial human uses of other species? If so, where do we draw the line, and what activities would be impermissibly trivial?

2. Do all species have equal "rights" to exist, or *must* some species be sacrificed in order to promote human welfare?

3. If *your* survival required you to kill the last male and female members of an endangered species, would you kill them? If so, how could your actions be ethically justified?

4. Suppose we manage to save a species by captive breeding programs in zoos, but its natural habitat is irretrievably altered. Is the species really *saved*, or is a species in human captivity really no more than a curio item or relic?

Test Questions

Multiple Choice. Each of the following questions has one correct answer. Circle the letter corresponding to the choice you think best answers the question.

D   1.   Extinction of plants and animals:

     a. is a natural process and therefore of little concern to us.
     b. is brought about today primarily by pollution.
     c. has slowed in recent years and is likely to slow in the future.
     d. today is many times faster than natural extinction.

C   2   Alteration of habitat:

     a. is one of the least important factors contributing to extinction.
     b. was responsible for the near extinction of many whales.
     c. is the most important factor contributing to plant and animal extinction today.
     d. all of the above
     e. none of the above

F   3.   Efforts to save a species may not always work because:

     a. of illegal poaching.
     b. worldwide cooperation is missing.
     c. populations may be reduced below the level needed to successfully reproduce.
     d. a & b
     e. a & c
     f. a, b, & c

B   4.   Hunting for sport:

     a. is a major contributing factor in animal extinction.
     b. rarely causes extinction today because of careful management practices.
     c. frequently benefits wildlife populations by eliminating sick and aged animals.
     d. a & b
     e. b & c

C   5.   Which of the following is true regarding extinction?

    a.   Approximately 90 million species have become extinct during the course of evolution.
    b.   The rate of extinction prior to the industrial revolution was much greater than the present rate.
    c.   Many species that have become extinct naturally are represented today by their descendants.
    d.   none of the above

Fill in the Blank. For each of the following questions, fill in the blank with the appropriate word or phrase.

1.   The pesticide _____ causes egg-shell thinning in peregrine falcons and other predatory birds.

2.   A species accidentally or intentionally introduced into a new environment is called a(n) _____ species.

3.   Pollution of air and water alters the _____ environment required by many species for survival.

4.   Once covering an area about the size of the United States, tropical rain forests have been reduced by about _____ .

5.   In 1973, Congress passed a law called the _____ _____ Act, which attempts to preserve endangered species largely by protecting their habitat.

6.   The unintentional poisoning of waterfowl at Kesterson National Wildlife Refuge was due to selenium which came from _____ .

7.   Organisms may be classified as _____ or specialists, the latter of which tend to be more prone to extinction.

8.   _____ _____ management utilizes a variety of techniques to preserve plants and wildlife.

9.   Critical species whose extinction may lead to ecosystem collapse are called _____ species.

10. The Tennessee Valley Authority's Tellico Dam on the Little Tennessee River raised the furor of the environmental community because it threatened the _____ _____ .

Answers: 1. DDT   2. foreign or alien   3. abiotic   4. one third   5. Endangered Species
6. irrigation water draining from farms   7. generalists   8. Integrated species   9. keystone
10. snail darter

Short Essay. Write a 250-300 word essay to answer each of the following questions.

1.   Describe the benefits of natural predators to a prey population.

2.   Do humans have the same beneficial effects that natural predators have on prey populations? Why or why not?

3.   Summarize the major factors that contribute to animal and plant extinction. Which ones are the most important?

4.   Why save endangered species?

Suggested Readings and Resource Materials

Kaufman, Les and Kenneth Mallory, Eds. (1987). *The Last Extinction*. Massachusetts: MIT Press. Compilation of interesting essays and case studies.

McNeely, Jeffrey, et al. (1990). *Conserving the World's Biological Diversity*. New York: World Resources Institute. Targeted at the general reader interested in biodiversity issues.

Norton, Bryan G. (1986). *The Preservation of Species*. New Jersey: Princeton University Press. A multidisciplinary analysis of a pressing problem, by a noted environmental philosopher.

Norton, Bryan G. (1987). *Why Preserve Natural Variety?* New Jersey: Princeton University Press. A philosophical examination of the justifications for species preservation.

Reid, W. V. C. and Kenton Miller (1989). *Keeping Options Alive: The Scientific Basis for the Conservation of Biodiversity*. New York: World Resources Institute. Examines the fundamental problems of and recommends policies for the preservation of biodiversity.

Soulé, Michael E. (1987). *Viable Populations for Conservation*. Massachusetts: Cambridge University Press. Integrates recent research in conservation biology with that in population biology.

Wilson, E. O. (1988). *Biodiversity*. National Academy Press. A compilation of articles by more than 60 experts on biodiversity. Excellent overview.

Videos: For ordering information, see Film/Video Index.

Greed and Wildlife: Poaching in America. Examines illegal slaughter of wildlife, primarily in the Great Smokey Mountains and Utah. Contact National Audubon Video/Inovision.

Plants in Peril highlights the problems and consequences of plant species extinction. Contact Films for the Humanities & Sciences, Inc.

CHAPTER 9

RANGELAND, FOREST, AND WILDERNESS: PRESERVING RENEWABLE RESOURCES

Outline

I. A TRAGEDY OF THE COMMONS

II. RANGELANDS AND RANGE MANAGEMENT
   A. Rangeland Deterioration
   B. Range Management

III. FORESTS AND FOREST MANAGEMENT
   A. Worldwide Deforestation
   B. Forest Conservation in the United States
   C. Forest Harvest and Management
   D. Prospects for the Future: Building a Sustainable System
      1. What Causes Deforestation?
      2. Increasing Wood Supply by Protecting Forests
      3. Increasing Supply by Reducing Waste
      4. Decreasing Demand: The Personal Connection

IV. WILDERNESS
   A. Preservation: The Wilderness Act
   B. Controversy Over Wilderness Designation
   C. The Wilderness Curse

Objectives

After studying this chapter, the student should be able to:

1. Define *commons* and identify the "*tragedy*" in Hardin's tragedy of the commons.
2. Discuss *rangeland* problems and possible management-based solutions.
3. Discuss *forest* problems and possible management-based solutions.
4. See *deforestation* as a global problem with a multitude of interrelated causes and a wide variety of effects.
5. Briefly recap the history of federal *forest protection* programs in the U.S.
6. Distinguish the forest management practices of *clearcutting*, *selective cutting*, and *shelterwood cutting*.
7. Summarize the major arguments pro and con *wilderness preservation*.

Lecture Notes

I. A TRAGEDY OF THE COMMONS
- A *commons* is any public commodity or resource.
- The *tragedy of the commons* is that individuals are compelled to abuse a commons in pursuit of personal gain.
- *Privately-owned land* is often similarly abused; again, the lure of short-term profits compels some to ignore long-term damage.

II. RANGELANDS AND RANGE MANAGEMENT
- *Rangelands* and their products are potentially *renewable resources*, if properly managed; if not, they can be ruined.

   A. Rangeland Deterioration
- Most rangeland in the U.S., both federal and private, has deteriorated due to *overuse* and *mismanagement*.

   B. Range Management
- One technique in *range management* is *grazing management*; another, *range improvement*, can help remediate past damage and restore productivity.
- Proper management respects a rangeland's *carrying capacity*.
- The Public Rangelands Improvement Act of 1978 is a first step towards reducing damage and developing sustainable rangeland management practices in the U.S.

III. FORESTS AND FOREST MANAGEMENT
- Forests are a *renewable resource* only to the extent that their renewal systems remain healthy; that's the major aim of *forest management* today.

   A. Worldwide Deforestation
- Clearing for *agriculture*, *firewood*, and *commercial use* has destroyed 30-50% of the world's forests.

   B. Forest Conservation in the United States
- *Yellowstone Timberland Reserve*, set aside in 1891, was the first national forest in the U.S.
- The *U.S. Forest Service* (U.S.F.S.) was established by *Pres. Roosevelt* in 1905 and headed by noted forest conservationist *Gifford Pinchot*.
- By law, U.S.F.S. lands are to be managed in accordance with the 1960 *Multiple Use/ Sustained Yield Act* which mandates management for all reasonable uses and for sustainability; in practice, these ideals are often not achieved.

   C. Forest Harvest and Management
- *Clearcutting* is the complete removal of trees from a tract of land.
- While sometimes benefitting certain game species, this practice more often *damages habitat* by accelerating erosion, surface runoff, and sedimentation.
- *Selective cutting* involves the removal of select trees from an otherwise more-or-less intact forest.
- Properly employed, selective harvesting is the least environmentally damaging method of tree harvest, though improper application may damage a forest over the long term.
- *Shelter-wood cutting*, while sometimes more expensive, is a sound management practice for sustainable forestry.

D. Prospects for the Future: Building a Sustainable System
   1. What Causes Deforestation?
      - *Deforestation* has a multitude of causes, including *government policies, economic priorities* and *incentives*, and *inefficient/ineffective market* and *legal systems.*

   2. Increasing Wood Supply by Protecting Forests
      - Forests managed properly and protected from excessive human and natural damage can *increase* our supply of wood.
      - While *forest fire suppression* can increase wood supplies in the short run, it may ultimately upset ecosystem balance and reduce wood supplies in the long run.

   3. Increasing Supply by Reducing Waste
      - More *efficient utilization* of harvested trees can reduce the total number of trees which we must cut from our forests.

   4. Decreasing Demand: The Personal Connection
      - Increased reliance on reusables and paper recycling can reduce the demand for virgin forest products.

IV. WILDERNESS
   - *Wilderness* holds a variety of values for us, including aesthetic, recreational, economic, and spiritual benefits.

   A. Preservation: The Wilderness Act
      - Passed in 1964, the *Wilderness Act* seeks to preserve certain lands in perpetual wilderness.

   B. Controversy Over Wilderness Designation
      - Some argue that preservationists are elitists, and pit *wilderness protection* against *economic development.*
      - Less than 4% of all U.S. land is protected as wilderness.

   C. The Wilderness Curse
      - Wilderness *crowding* and *overuse* can degrade its quality; proper visitor and resource management can minimize these problems.

Case Study

Off-Road Vehicles: Solving the Conflicts Among Land Users

In 1947, in the bomb-shattered city of Hamamatsu, Japan, a 41-year-old college dropout and mechanic named Soichiro was rummaging through the debris when he found a surplus field generator. He took it home, strapped it to his bicycle, and with some additional tinkering had a motorbike. Soon afterward, Soichiro was designing motorbikes and motorcycles bearing his last name, Honda. By 1960 Honda was selling motorcycles in the United States, and by 1976 he had captured half of the U.S. market, selling hundreds of thousands of motorcycles each year. Honda's success was twofold. For one, the company sold well-built machines that were dependable and easy to repair. It also mounted a wide advertising campaign to clean up the image of the motorcycle user. Ads featured well-dressed, respectable-looking actors to convey the notion that decent, law-abiding Americans could also enjoy a motorcycle as transportation and a source of recreation.

The motorcycle movement grew quickly. In the early 1960s there were only 400,000 registered motorcycles in the United States, but by 1987 the number had grown to over 5 million, two-thirds of which are used off the road at some time. Snowmobiles had a similar explosive growth. They were introduced to the public in 1959. Today there are about 3 million in the United States and Canada. Dune buggies, four-wheel-drive vehicles, and the latest, all-terrain vehicles, join the legion of off-road vehicles meandering up mountain roads, tearing across open fields, and sloshing through muddy streams. Today there are an estimated 250,000 dune buggies and over 3 million four-wheel-drive vehicles, half of which are used off the road at some time in their life. All-terrain vehicles number nearly 4 million.

The off-road-vehicle (ORV) craze struck almost without warning, prompted by advertisements that showed drivers conquering steep slopes, charging through streams, and crashing through mud. Public land managers were surprised with the sudden explosion of off-road vehicles, and private landowners were often irate to find their property inundated by these sometimes-noisy and often-destructive machines. Today, over 45 million Americans engage in this sport, and 50% of all off-road vehicle use occurs on federal land. As ORV popularity climbed, so did the conflicts. Private landowners, public land managers, recreationists, environmentalists, and scientists complained that the use of ORVs damaged plants and soils, conflicted with other forms of recreation, and adversely affected wildlife.

Snowmobiles damage the environment less than most other off-road vehicles, but their impact can be significant. Their noise, for example, disturbs wildlife, homeowners, and other recreationists, especially snowshoers and cross-country skiers. Snowmobiles compact the snow they travel on. In popular snowmobiling areas in Minnesota, scientists have noted that compacted snow is turned to ice and that this ice melts one week later than unpacked snow in the vicinity. This, they speculate, shortens the growing season for plants and could reduce plant growth overall. Compacted snow is also a poorer insulator than uncompacted snow; thus, in areas frequented by snowmobiles, the soil freezes to a greater depth. The deep freezing may harm the roots of small plants and trees. Tree seedlings are easily damaged by snowmobiles. Commercial tree growers report that snowmobiles break off the tops of trees; this may not kill them, but often causes them to grow crooked, reducing their value for timber.

By compacting the snow, snowmobiles also impair the movement of rodents that burrow at the interface between the snow and the ground (subnivean space) during the winter in search of food. One study showed a doubling of mortality among rodents in an area used by snowmobiles. Packing snow on lakes may decrease light transmission through the ice by making the ice more opaque. This, scientists say, could reduce what little photosynthesis occurs during the winter. Snowmobiles offer hunters and anglers access to remote areas during the winter, where they may overfish and overhunt certain species. For example, one group of 150 snowmobilers invaded a back-country lake in Minnesota and in one day removed 280 kilograms (560 pounds) of fish, nearly the entire population of the lake. Finally, a small minority of snowmobilers harass wild animals. Chasing these cold-stressed animals can deplete their marginal energy supplies. In a weakened state, they can fall prey to predators, disease, and cold.

Snowmobile damage can be reduced in a number of ways. First, users must exercise self-restraint and avoid areas that could be adversely affected, especially alpine tundra, private land, stands of new trees, and critical wildlife habitat. Second, special trails can be developed so snowmobiles will not bother other recreationists and wildlife. In Rocky Mountain National Park, for instance, snowmobilers are allowed to use the main highways, which in winter are closed to other vehicles, but they are kept apart from cross-country skiers. Third, snowmobile clubs can educate their members not to harass wildlife and to act reasonably around other recreationists. Members should be discouraged from using their snowmobiles when there is less than 15 centimeters (6 inches) of snow on the ground. Fourth, quieter snowmobiles could be developed. Everyone, including the users, will benefit (see Chapter Supplement 15-4 on noise pollution). Fifth, land managers must do a better job of regulating hunting and fishing in remote areas that are accessible to snowmobilers.

Four-wheel-drive vehicles, dune buggies, motorcycles, and all-terrain vehicles do considerably more damage than snowmobiles, because there are more of them and because they are used at a time when there is no protective layer over the soil and vegetation. ORVs have damaged land from Florida to Maine and from New York to California. No ecosystem has been spared. The alpine tundra of the Rocky Mountains and the Sierra Nevada and the arctic tundra of Alaska all bear their imprints. Wooded areas in Florida, Indiana, Missouri, and Colorado are scarred by inconsiderate ORV users. The grasslands of Kansas and Montana show the signs of damage. In some places, the damage will be repaired naturally; in others, where damage is severe, natural repair cannot occur. Tiny trails turn into deep gullies that worsen with time.

ORVs scar land, destroy plants, accelerate soil erosion, alter the physical and chemical characteristics of soil, impair revegetation, damage wildlife habitat, destroy wildlife, and conflict with other recreationists. Especially hard hit are the wild and semi-wild areas around many western cities such as Albuquerque, Phoenix, Denver, Las Vegas, San Francisco, and Los Angeles. The major problem with ORV use is that the terrain that most challenges the users and is, therefore, the most attractive to them is also most sensitive to erosion. Large areas of the American desert, coastal sand dunes, barrier islands, forests, grasslands, and tundra are dissected and rutted by ORVs. In the tire-torn deserts of the west, archaeological resources are being badly damaged. In particular, intaglios, large human and animal figures carved into the earth by ancient people, are being badly scarred by tire tracks. Today, citizens working with the BLM are fencing off these areas to prevent further damage to these precious remnants of past cultures.

Vegetation is particularly hard hit by ORVs. Roots, seedlings, and foliage of small plants are crushed by tires. Plants are uprooted. Frames of ORVs tear limbs off larger plants. ORV damage has a ripple effect: When plants are destroyed, the soil's organic content falls, which decreases water retention and subsequent plant growth. In addition, destroying vegetation reduces ground cover and habitat for animals, increases soil erosion, and changes soil temperature, with many long-term consequences.

Of the impacts of ORVs, soil erosion is generally the most severe. Trails used by ORVs for six years near Santa Cruz, California, are now gullies 3 meters (10 feet) deep. In other areas of California, land used by ORV drivers for fewer than ten years has been so severely eroded that the bedrock is exposed. Erosion on trails removes topsoil and uproots trees and shrubs along the border of the trails. The sediment washed away by running water is deposited downstream in river beds and on vegetation. OVRs also compact the soil from 1 to 3 meters (3 to 10 feet) below the surface on popular trails. This compaction zone impairs root growth and impedes the penetration of water, thus diminishing plant growth and recharge of underground water supplies. Loss of shade-providing vegetation and the compaction of soil both contribute to a decrease in soil moisture in many areas; soil moisture may be decreased by 43% as deep as 3 meters below the surface on silt and clay soils. On hilly terrain, the loss of vegetation increases water and wind erosion, often with devastating effects. ORVs destabilize sand dunes by destroying plants that naturally stabilize the sand. Moreover, once soils have begun to erode, reestablishing plants and regenerating the topsoil may become impossible. When soils can be revegetated, the costs run as high as $8,000 to $24,000 per hectare.

ORVs destroy the habitat of reptiles and mammals. Populations of ground-nesting birds, such as the California quail and snowy plover, can be wiped out. Large races with hundreds of motorcycles tearing across the deserts of the West are the most environmentally damaging of all ORV activities. Recognizing the impact of ORVs, President Nixon signed an executive order to limit their use on public land. President Carter amended this in 1977 to mandate closure of public lands to ORVs where they could cause damage or have caused damage to soil, vegetation, wildlife, and other values. In response to the executive orders, the Forest Service developed 150 ORV management plans for its lands. The BLM also developed regulations, but it has dragged its feet in implementing them. The BLM regulations made it possible for land managers to designate lands as either open, restricted, or closed to ORVs. Both the BLM and Forest Service regulations have made inroads into the problem of ORV damage. In addition, ORV users have banded together and made considerable strides to educate their members on ways to reduce damage and minimize conflict with other recreationists.

But ORV damage still occurs. Some people continue to violate rules and common sense. Recent federal budget cuts will reduce governmental surveillance of sensitive areas and rehabilitation projects. In light of declining federal budgets for land management, some experts say that ORV users themselves must patrol their activities, increase education, and learn to act more responsibly. Volunteer groups could pitch in to repair eroded trails. Increased state and federal taxes on ORVs could be used to fund management and enforcement personnel. Increased penalties for violations of ORV regulations could also help fund management and enforcement. More efforts are needed to separate ORVs from other recreationists, especially hikers and cross-country skiers. Tighter regulations that prohibit ORV use in areas where it adversely affects wildlife, homeowners, nonmotorized recreationists, archaeological resources, vegetation, and soil are also needed. Governmental officials could develop special areas for ORVs. These could be used on a rotating basis to minimize damage and allow time for recovery. More programs are needed to educate ORV users on their impact and ways they can minimize it. Even basic lessons on the value of preserving the wild areas and maintaining ecological stability might help schoolchildren learn to act more responsibly.

ORVs are here to stay, say their supporters. They're a legitimate form of recreation. Many of their opponents agree: If their use can be better regulated, why not let them stay? But the price will be restraint, an exercise of common sense that reduces the damage and keeps incompatible forms of recreation well apart from one another.

Critical Thinking Problems

1. Arguments against designation of additional wilderness areas today generally rest on claims of lost economic opportunities. If we accept the premise that economic development should take precedence over preservation, how can we justify expenditures for art galleries, museums, libraries, and theatres, which, like wilderness areas, admittedly are not "cost-effective" and can also be said to cater to the "elite"?

2. Is the tragedy of the commons *inevitable* wherever individuals have access to public resources? Would appeals to conscience alleviate the problem? Why or why not?

3. We know that no ecosystems are static. Hence, can our efforts to forever "preserve" wilderness in its present state be characterized as "unnatural"?

Test Questions

Multiple Choice. Each of the following questions has one correct answer. Circle the letter corresponding to the choice you think best answers the question.

D   1. Rangelands:

     a. are a more energy-intensive way of growing beef than feedlots.
     b. reduce the amount of grain needed to feed livestock.
     c. in the United States are mostly found west of the Mississippi River.
     d. b & c
     e. a & c

C   2. Which of the following is the most significant cause of damage to rangelands?

     a. fires
     b. drought
     c. overgrazing
     d. insect pests

B   3. The Multiple Use/Sustained Yield Act of 1960:

     a. pertained only to National Forests.
     b. promoted wise use of forests and grasslands for long-term benefits to private and commercial interests.
     c. required that all federal agencies write an environmental impact statement before embarking on any development on federal land.

A.   4. Clearcutting of forests:

     a. can be made aesthetically appealing if cuts are kept small and made to blend with the natural terrain.
     b. is the only economically feasible way of cutting most hardwoods.
     c. will not work for trees that tolerate lots of sunlight.
     d. is a three-step technique that does only a small amount of damage to the forest.

D   5. The Wilderness Act of 1964:

     a. established the National Wilderness Preservation System.
     b. added 23 million hectares of Alaskan wilderness to the existing wilderness system.
     c. sought to establish an enduring wilderness while still allowing livestock grazing and mining for fuel and metals.
     d. a & c
     e. b & c

Fill in the Blank. For each of the following questions, fill in the blank with the appropriate word or phrase.

1.   There are two general ways to manage rangelands: range improvement and
    _____ management.

2. Removal of mature trees from a forest is a technique practiced in hardwood stands and is called
   _____ _____.

3. _____ _____ are managed like modern farms; plots are planted with seedlings, fertilized, and sprayed with herbicides to control undesirable species.

4. _____ _____ are started each year to control the build up of underbrush and runaway fires.

5. The Wilderness Act converted Forest Service _____ areas into wilderness areas.

6. Garrett Hardin popularized the idea of the _____ ____ _____ _____.

7. Forestry scientists estimate that somewhere between _____ and _____ percent of the world's forests have been destroyed by humankind.

8. President _____ _____ established the first forest reserve, known as the Yellowstone Timberland Reserve, in 1891.

9. President _____ _____ established the Forest Service in 1905.

10. Most animals can escape the periodic, minor _____ fires that burn off dead branches and other materials that have accumulated on the forest floor.

Answers: 1. grazing 2. selective cutting (or silviculture) 3. Tree farms 4. Prescribed fires
5. primitive 6. tragedy of the commons 7. 30, 50 8. Benjamin Harrison 9. Theodore Roosevelt
10. ground

Short Essay. Write a 250-300 word essay to answer each of the following questions.

1. Garrett Hardin wrote about communal pastureland, the commons, shared by English cattleranchers. What central point did he make about the commons? How does that apply to air, water, and land today? Do you think that his thesis is entirely accurate and applies only to land held in common?

2. Why does the Forest Service let many natural forest fires burn, rather than extinguish them?

3. State the opposing viewpoints on wilderness designation.

Suggested Readings and Resource Materials

Pyne, Stephen J. "The Summer We Let Wildfire Loose" in *Natural History*, August 1989, pp. 48-49. Illustrates the difficulties inherent in attempts to preserve ecosystems in a freeze-frame "static" condition.

Repetto, Robert and Malcolm Gillis, Eds. (1988). *Public Policy and the Misuse of Forest Resources.* New York: World Resources Institute. Explores the role of government policy in encouraging tropical deforestation projects.

Sierra Club (1982). *Our Public Lands: An Introduction to the Agencies and Issues.* San Francisco: Sierra Club Books. Good overview.

World Resources Institute (1985). *Tropical Forests: A Call for Action.* New York: World Resources Institute. An international task force report.

WorldWatch Institute. *Reforesting the Earth.* Washington, DC: WorldWatch Institute.

Videos: For ordering information, see Film/Video Index.

Banking On Disaster. World Bank programs and U.S. tax dollars subsidizing destruction of Amazon rainforest. Contact Bullfrog Films.

Earth First! The Struggle for the Australian Rainforest. Highlights the plight of our most ancient treasures, the rainforests. Contact The Video Project.

Jungle Burger. Covers the fast-food hamburger/rainforest destruction connection. Contact Barfuss Films.

Our Threatened Heritage. Excellent videotape on destruction of tropical forests. Contact National Wildlife Federation.

The Ancient Forests. Visual documentation of clearcutting in the Pacific Northwest. Contact Project Lighthawk.

Vanishing Earth. Examines deforestation, soil erosion, desertification, and salinization on several continents. Contact BBC Enterprises.

CHAPTER 10

WATER RESOURCES:
PRESERVING OUR LIQUID ASSETS

Outline

I. THE HYDROLOGICAL CYCLE

II. WATER SUPPLIES AND USAGE
   A. The Global Picture
   B. Water Use in the United States

III. MISMANAGING OUR WATER RESOURCES: CAUSES AND CONSEQUENCES
   A. The Numbers Game: Beyond Drought
   B. Overdraft: Depleting Our Liquid Assets
   C. Are We Flooding Our Own Homes?
      1. Causes of Flooding
      2. Controlling Flooding

IV. PROTECTING OUR LIQUID ASSETS
   A. Population Control
   B. Technical Solutions: Costs and Benefits
      1. Dams and Reservoirs
      2. Water Diversion Projects
      3. Desalination
      4. Groundwater Management
      5. Conservation and Recycling
   C. Doing Your Share: Personal Solutions
   D. Education Solutions
   E. Legal Solutions

V. CHAPTER SUPPLEMENT. WETLANDS, ESTUARIES, COASTLINES, AND RIVERS
   A. Wetlands
      1. The Hidden Value of Wetlands
      2. Declining Wetlands
      3. Protecting Wetlands
   B. Estuaries
      1. Damaging this Important Zone
      2. Protecting the Estuarine Zone
   C. Coastlines and Barrier Islands
   D. Wild and Scenic Rivers

Objectives

After studying this chapter, the student should be able to:

1. Trace and explain the *hydrological cycle.*
2. Characterize the major aspects of *water supply* and *usage.*
3. Discuss the factors which contribute to *mismanagement* of water resources.
4. Identify the *causes* of flooding and possible flood-control strategies.
5. Outline a *water resources management plan* which integrates sound techniques for protecting our supplies.
6. Discuss *wetlands, estuaries, coastlines,* and *barrier islands* and the major threats to them today.
7. Cite the major arguments pro and con protecting free-flowing rivers under the *Wild and Scenic Rivers Act.*

Lecture Notes

I. THE HYDROLOGICAL CYCLE
   - The *hydrological* or global water cycle consists of two phases, *evaporation* and *precipitation.*
   - The cycle is driven by *winds* generated by *solar energy.*

II. WATER SUPPLIES AND USAGE

   A. The Global Picture
      - Water *shortages* and *quality problems* occur in nearly every region of the world.
      - *Contaminated water supplies* cause serious health problems in underdeveloped areas.
      - *Water shortages* are a function of *uneven distribution* and *increased demand* due to human population growth.
      - *Agriculture* is by far the largest user of water worldwide, followed by industrial and domestic use.

   B. Water Use in the United States
      - Per capita water consumption in the U.S. averages *5700 liters* (1500 gallons) *per day.*

III. MISMANAGING OUR WATER RESOURCES: CAUSES AND CONSEQUENCES

   A. The Numbers Game: Beyond Drought
      - *Natural factors, mismanagement,* and *overpopulation* all contribute to water shortages.
      - While *droughts* appear to be natural causes of water shortages, human activities may increase their frequency and severity.

   B. Overdraft: Depleting Our Liquid Assets
      - Water shortages can be addressed two ways: *increase supply* or *decrease demand*
      - Efforts to increase supply often have devastating *ecological effects* including *saltwater intrusion, habitat destruction, aquifer depletion,* and *subsidence.*

   C. Are We Flooding Our Own Homes?
      1. Causes of Flooding
         - *Human activities* and *land use patterns* combine with heavy precipitation and other natural factors to produce floods.

2. Controlling Flooding
   - *Structural flood-control* devices and *watershed management* are two different approaches to controlling flooding.
   - *Stream channelization* is an environmentally destructive technique for draining wetlands and reducing flooding.

IV. PROTECTING OUR LIQUID ASSETS

A. Population Control
   - *Reduced population growth* will lessen demand in water-short regions.

B. Technical Solutions: Costs and Benefits
   1. Dams and Reservoirs
      - Though beneficial in many respects, *dams* have severe sociological and ecological impacts.
   2. Water Diversion Projects
      - These projects decrease stream flow and increase *sedimentation* and *salination*.
   3. Desalination
      - The removal of *salt* from sea or brackish water to produce freshwater can be accomplished through *evaporation* or *reverse osmosis*.
      - *Energy* and *capital/operating costs* of desalination remain high.
   4. Groundwater Management
      - This technique can help *recharge groundwater supplies* and *reduce withdrawals*.
   5. Conservation and Recycling
      - Increasingly, shortages will be met not by expanding supplies but by *water conservation* and *recycling*, especially in agriculture and industry.

C. Doing Your Share: Personal Solutions
   - Personal behavior modification can reduce our water use.

D. Education Solutions
   - *Education* can increase society's awareness of the value of natural resources, including water.

E. Legal Solutions
   - New *laws, codes,* and *pricing schedules* can substantially reduce demand for water.

V. CHAPTER SUPPLEMENT. WETLANDS, ESTUARIES, COASTLINES, AND RIVERS

A. Wetlands
   - These are *flooded lands* lying either *inland* or in *coastal* zones.
   1. The Hidden Value of Wetlands
      - Wetlands function as valuable *habitats* and *water-quality protectors*.
   2. Declining wetlands
      - Wetlands are destroyed in the U.S. and elsewhere for *development* and *agriculture*.
   3. Protecting Wetlands
      - Various federal and state *bills* are designed to *protect* remaining wetlands in the U.S., though enforcement, and thus effectiveness, is low.

B. Estuaries
    - *Estuaries*, or river mouths and bays, are critical habitat for many commercial species and wildlife.
    - Estuarine zones are valuable also as *water purifiers*.
    1. Damaging This Important Zone
        - *Pollution, sedimentation, inflow reduction,* and *dredging/filling projects* all harm estuarine zones and their life forms.
    2. Protecting the Estuarine Zone
        - *Pollution* and *erosion control,* along with *water conservation,* will help protect the estuarine zone.

C. Coastlines and Barrier Islands
    - *Barrier islands* form in response to *wave* and *wind patterns* offshore.
    - *Development* and *beach-erosion-control* programs threaten both barrier islands and coastal beaches.

D. Wild and Scenic Rivers
    - The few remaining *free-flowing* and *undeveloped rivers* in the U.S. may be eligible for protection under the *Wild and Scenic Rivers Act.*

Critical Thinking Problems

1. In order to fairly allocate scarce water supplies, government must somehow rank or prioritize water demands. On what basis can we assign differing values to competing water needs? Is there a way to distinguish necessary from trivial demands?

2. Suppose that a proposed water project will increase the supply of water to a town in an arid region so that the residents can irrigate their lush, green lawns and golf courses. Suppose too that this project will require damming that last free-flowing stretch of a nearby river, but that the project is unanimously supported by the area's residents and political representatives and will be paid for by the water's users. Assuming that the project's species impact will be minimal, can you find a good reason to oppose the project?

Test Questions

Multiple Choice. Each of the following questions has one correct answer. Circle the letter corresponding to the choice you think best answers the question.

C. 1. At any moment ____ percent of the earth's water is found in the oceans.

    a. 50
    b. 75
    c. 94
    d. 99

B. 2. Which of the following is true about water?

    a. The United States withdraws 25% of its freshwater from rivers and lakes.
    b. Agriculture uses about 47% of the water withdrawn from surface and groundwater supplies in the Unites States.
    c. Clouds contain large quantities of impurities carried from the ground's surface with evaporating water.
    d. As a rule, it is economically feasible for a country to withdraw up to 50% of its annual stream flow.

C. 3. Desalination of salt water:

    a. is inexpensive and widely used today to provide drinking water.
    b. is technically difficult.
    c. produces water that is four times as expensive as current water supply methods.
    d. would be an excellent way of supplying water to agricultural regions of the midwest.

B. 4. Concerning global water supply:

    a. few nations face water shortages.
    b. three out of every four people in developing nations do not have access to clean, disease-free drinking water.
    c. few nations will face water shortages by the year 2000.
    d. it is generally feasible for a nation to withdraw up to 50% of a stream's or river's annual flow.

D. 5. Flooding:

    a. is worsened by stripping land of vegetation and construction of homes.
    b. can be lessened by removing vegetation, a technique which allows more water to penetrate into the ground.
    c. is less likely if rain falls at a slow rate.
    d. a & c
    e. b & c

Fill in the Blank. For each of the following questions, fill in the blank with the appropriate word or phrase.

1. The _____ cycle is a natural system for collecting, purifying, and distributing water throughout the world.

2. The loss of water from soil and leaves is called _____.

3. Overexploitation of groundwater in coastal areas can result in _____ _____, the movement of salt water into freshwater aquifers.

4. The amount of runoff that can be counted on from year to year is called the _____ runoff.

5. In _____ _____, water is purified by passing it through thin membranes that hold back contaminants.

6. A drought occurs, by definition, when rainfall is 70% below normal for a period of _____ days or longer.

7. Sinking of the surface as a result of groundwater depletion is called _____.

8. _____ management is to flood control what preventive medicine is to health care.

9. Straightening a streambed is called streambed _____.

10. Dams reduce waterflow to the ocean, and reduced _____ inflow often negatively affects estuarine aquatic life.

Answers: 1. hydrological (water) 2. evapotranspiration 3. saltwater intrusion 4. stable 5. reverse osmosis 6. 21 7. subsidence 8. Watershed 9. channelization 10. nutrient (or sediment)

Short Essay. Write a 250-300 word essay to answer each of the following questions.

1. Describe what happens to moisture-laden air as it flows over a mountain range.

2. Who uses most of the water in the United States? What efforts can be made to cut back on water usage by these users?

3. What environmental impacts do dams have? What are some alternatives to increase water supply and which ones are the most ecologically sound?

4. Describe the problems caused by the Bureau of Reclamation in the Kissimmee River's watershed.

Chapter Supplement. Wetlands, Estuaries, Coastlines, and Rivers

Multiple Choice. Each of the following questions has one correct answer. Circle the letter corresponding to the choice you think best answers the question.

E   1. Wetlands:

    a. are areas of high productivity.
    b. hold water after rainfall and reduce flooding.
    c. generally hold back sediment eroded from the land and keep streams cleaner.
    d. are being destroyed at a rate of about 120,000 hectares or 300,000 acres per year in the United States.
    e. all of the above
    f. none of the above

A   2. The estuarine zone:

    a. is the home of two-thirds of all commercial and noncommercial fish during some part of their life cycle.
    b. is a region of low productivity because of high siltation.
    c. can be drastically affected by dams which hold back sediment.

E   3.   The narrow islands lying off the Atlantic and Gulf coasts:

   a. are called barrier islands.
   b. are stable islands good for home sites.
   c. grow and shrink from year to year.
   d. stand high enough out of the water so that winter storms do little damage to buildings, roadways and other structures.
   e. a & c
   f. b & c

Fill in the Blank. For each of the following questions, fill in the blank with the appropriate word or phrase.

1.   Mangrove swamps, salt marshes, bays, and lagoons are all _____ wetlands.

2.   The mouths of rivers where salt and fresh water mix are called _____.

3.   Wind creates _____ _____ currents that run parallel to beaches.

4.   The _____ _____ _____ _____ Act of 1968 was established to prevent construction along some of this country's remaining free-flowing rivers.

Answers: 1. coastal   2. estuaries   3. long shore   4. Wild and Scenic Rivers

Suggested Readings and Resource Materials

Reisner, Marc (1986). *Cadillac Desert.* New York: Viking. A thorough examination and exposé of water problems, projects, and policies in the American West.

Postel, Sandra. *Water: Rethinking Management in an Age of Scarcity.* Washington, DC: WorldWatch Institute.

Reisner, Marc and Sara Bates (1990). *Overtapped Oasis.* Washington, DC: Island Press. Focuses on inefficiency of western water use and its causes.

El-Ashry, M.T. and D.C. Gibbons (1986). *Troubled Waters: New Policies for Managing Water in the American West.* Washington, DC: World Resources Institute.

Videos: For ordering information, see Film/Video Index.

Water Wars: California. Focuses on water struggles in California and their historical roots. Contact Cine Research Associates.

Water and Life: A Delicate Balance. Good overview of water use, pollution, and availability. Contact Films for the Humanities & Sciences.

CHAPTER 11

ENERGY:
WINNING A DANGEROUS GAME

Outline

I.   THE FOSSIL FUEL CONNECTION: DISCOVERING OUR ENERGY DEPENDENCE

II. ENERGY USE -- THEN AND NOW

III. IMPACTS OF ENERGY PRODUCTION AND CONSUMPTION

IV. ENERGY TRENDS: SUPPLIES AND DEMANDS
    A. Oil: The End Is Near
    B. Natural Gas: A Better Outlook
    C. Coal: The Brightest but the Dirtiest?

V.   OUR ENERGY FUTURE
    A. Hard Paths and Soft Paths
    B. Guidelines for Wise Decisions
        1. Ensuring Positive Net Energy Production
        2. Energy Matching
        3. Converting Energy Efficiently
        4. Reducing Pollution and Ensuring Safety
        5. Ensuring Abundance and Renewability
        6. Affordability
    C. Abandoning the Old

Objectives

After studying this chapter, the student should be able to:

1. Trace the *history* of energy use and the development of fossil fuel dependence in the U.S.
2. Discuss the *energy fuel cycle* for coal or oil and identify the points at which human and environmental impacts are generated.
3. Understand the complex relations between energy *supply, demand,* and *price.*
4. Give approximate timetables for *depletion* of fossil fuels at current rates of consumption.
5. Distinguish and discuss the pros and cons of the *hard* versus the *soft energy paths.*
6. Outline a set of *criteria* which any *adequate, environmentally* and *economically progressive* energy plan must meet.

Lecture Notes

I. THE FOSSIL FUEL CONNECTION: DISCOVERING OUR ENERGY DEPENDENCE
    - *Fossil fuels* are rising in cost as supplies dwindle; the *economic implications* of severe fuel price increases are staggering.
    - The *"energy crises"* of the 1970s shook up oil importing nations, stimulating conservation and new energy research and technology.
    - Recent fuel *"gluts"* have engendered a false and dangerous sense of energy security.

II. ENERGY USE -- THEN AND NOW
    - In the past century, *wood* was our major fuel; today *oil, natural gas*, and *coal* provide most of our energy.
    - The U.S. accounts for *6%* of the world's population but uses *30%* of its energy; sheer *wastefulness* and *inefficiency* are partially to blame for this discrepancy.

III. IMPACTS OF ENERGY PRODUCTION AND CONSUMPTION
    - The *energy fuel cycle* impacts human and ecosystem health at several points: *exploration, extraction, processing, distribution*, and *end use*.
    - *Stripmining* and *tunnel mining* for coal have had considerable environmental impacts on large regions of the U.S.; impacts include *erosion, habitat loss, siltation, acid drainage*, and *land subsidence*.
    - *Transporting* and *burning coal* produces a variety of air and water pollution and solid waste *pollution problems*.

IV. ENERGY TRENDS: SUPPLIES AND DEMANDS
    - As *demands* increase, finding adequate *supplies* becomes more difficult.

    A. Oil: The End Is Near
        - At current consumption rates, oil will be depleted in about 75 years.
        - As supplies decline, *prices* will rise dramatically and shortages will be more common.

    B. Natural Gas: A Better Outlook
        - *Global supplies* of natural gas are adequate for about a century at current use rates.
        - *Domestic production* has peaked, and prices will rise as supplies shrink further.

    C. Coal: The Brightest but the Dirtiest?
        - Our most *abundant* fossil fuel, coal supplies are adequate for hundreds of years more use, though at *heavy environmental cost*.

V. OUR ENERGY FUTURE

    A. Hard Path and Soft Paths
        - The *hard path* consists of *large, centralized, nonrenewable* energy sources; its proponents place their faith in a *technological fix* to cure our energy problems.
        - The *soft path*, as described by Amory Lovins, relies on *conservation* and *renewable energy* sources in a *diversified, decentralized* system.

    B. Guidelines for Wise Decisions
        1. Ensuring Positive Net Energy Production
            - This means that *energy gained* should always exceed *energy spent* in extraction, transportation, and conversion.

2. Energy Matching
   - *Matching* energy *sources* and *needs* can dramatically increase efficiency.
3. Converting Energy Efficiently
   - By keeping the *laws of thermodynamics* in mind, *conversion efficiency* can be raised and energy supplies extended.
4. Reducing Pollution and Ensuring Safety
   - Energy sources should be as *environmentally benign* and *safe for humans* as possible.
5. Ensuring Abundance and Renewability
   - Both hard and soft path advocates urge a switch to *renewable* fuels in order to ensure long-term *abundance*.
6. Affordability
   - When all externalities, subsidies, and indirect costs have been factored in, the more *affordable* energy source will seem best suited for further development.

C. Abandoning the Old
   - A new policy for a *responsible, sustainable energy program* will almost certainly necessitate *abandonment* of old energy *allegiances* and *customs*.

Critical Thinking Problems

1. Suppose that we find a technological fix for every problem of pollution associated with the oil-fuel cycle. Would there still be good reasons to switch from oil to a renewable fuel source? (Hint: Remember that oil is a *material* for many products, such as pharmaceuticals, for which there are no known replacements).

2. Some have likened drilling for oil in the Arctic National Wildlife Refuge to breaking up the furniture for firewood. Does the proposal to drill in the ANWR smack of such desperation? Is such a country, willing to exploit its resources to the maximum, more properly called "rich" or "poor"?

Test Questions

Multiple Choice. Each of the following questions has one correct answer. Circle the letter corresponding to the choice you think best answers the question.

D 1. The United States' major source of energy today is:

   a. coal.
   b. natural gas.
   c. nuclear power.
   d. oil.

B 2. The United States has about 6% of the world's population but uses _____ of the global energy consumed every year.

   a. 20%
   b. 30%
   c. 50%
   d. 70%

A   3.   External cost refers to:

    a.   the cost of pollution borne by society and not by a manufacturer.
    b.   the cost of producing a good borne by the manufacturer.
    c.   the total cost of producing energy.
    d.   none of the above

B   4.   Acid mine drainage:

    a.   is prevalent in western states.
    b.   forms when water, air, and iron pyrite react.
    c.   consists mostly of nitric acid.
    d.   a & b
    e.   b & c
    f.   a & c

C   5.   Global energy consumption is about:

    a.   100 quads per year.
    b.   150 quads per year.
    c.   250 quads per year.
    d.   350 quads per year.

A   6.   At the current rate of consumption, the world's proven oil reserves will last about ____ years.

    a.   25
    b.   50
    c.   75
    d.   100

C   7.   Which of the following fossil fuels has the largest unused reserves?

    a.   oil
    b.   natural gas
    c.   coal
    d.   oil shale

E.   8.   The soft path refers to an energy strategy that is:

    a.   based on conservation and renewable resources.
    b.   centralized.
    c.   capital intensive.
    d.   labor intensive.
    e.   a & d
    f.   b & c

B   9.   Using energy efficiently requires:

    a.   use of high-quality energy for all of our tasks.
    b.   a good matching of the end uses with potential energy supplies.
    c.   ensuring a negative net energy yield.
    d.   none of the above

F   10. Most environmental damage in energy fuel systems comes from:

    a. storage.
    b. extraction.
    c. exploration.
    d. consumption.
    e. a & c
    f. b & d

Fill in the Blank. For each of the following questions, fill in the blank with the appropriate word or phrase.

1. Coal mines common in mountainous or hilly regions of the east are called _____ _____ mines.

2. Dirt and rock lying over a bed of coal is known as _____.

3. _____ _____ is a progressive, debilitating disease of the lungs caused by breathing dust in coal mines.

4. A fine dust known as _____ _____ is emitted from coal-fired power plants not equipped with adequate pollution control devices.

5. Sulfur dioxide emitted from coal-fired power plants can be removed by _____ _____.

Answers: 1. contour strip   2. overburden   3. Black Lung disease or pneumoconiosis   4. fly ash
5. smokestack scrubbers

Short Essay. Write a 250-300 word essay to answer each of the following questions.

1. Define the term "energy system" or "energy fuel cycle" and give an example.

2. Describe the United States' pattern of shifting energy dependency. What changes do you see in energy supply in the next 100 years?

3. Compare and contrast the hard and soft energy paths.

4. Discuss the guidelines presented in Chapter 11 for the wise use of energy.

5. Briefly discuss the factors that will determine how much energy we will need 100 years from now.

Suggested Readings and Resource Materials

Carrying Capacity (1986). *Beyond Oil: The Threat to Food and Fuel in the Coming Decades*. New York: Ballinger Publishing. Characterizes the threat to food and fuel in the near future as oil supplies dwindle.

Flavin, Christopher. *Nuclear Power: The Market Test*. Washington, DC: WorldWatch Institute.

Videos: For ordering information, see Film/Video Index.

Energy: The Dilemma. Summarizes the problems caused by our increasing demands for energy from oil, gas, coal, and nuclear power. Contact Churchill Films.

CHAPTER 12

FUTURE ENERGY:
MAKING THE BEST CHOICES

Outline

I. ESTABLISHING A SHOPPING LIST

II. NONRENEWABLE ENERGY SOURCES
    A. Nuclear Fission
        1. Nuclear Power: Pros and Cons
        2. Reactor Safety
        3. Waste Disposal
        4. Social Acceptability and Cost
        5. Proliferation of Nuclear Weapons
        6. Breeder Reactors
    B. Nuclear Fusion
    C. Coal
    D. Natural Gas
    E. Synthetic Fuels
        1. Oil Shale
        2. Tar Sands
        3. Coal Gasification and Liquefaction

III. RENEWABLE ENERGY RESOURCES
    A. Solar Energy
        1. Pros and Cons of Solar Energy
        2. Passive Solar Heating
        3. Active Solar
        4. Photovoltaics
    B. Wind
    C. Biomass
    D. Hydroelectric Power
    E. Geothermal Energy
    F. Hydrogen Fuel
    G. The Renewable Energy Potential

IV. CONSERVATION

V. BUILDING A SUSTAINABLE ENERGY SYSTEM
    A. Shifting to a Sustainable Transportation System
        1. Improving Efficiency
        2. From Road to Rails and Buses
        3. Economic Changes Accompanying a Shift to Mass Transit

VI. CHAPTER SUPPLEMENT. RADIATION POLLUTION
   A. How Is Radiation Measured?
   B. Source of Radiation
      1. Natural Sources
      2. Anthropogenic Sources
   C. Effects of Radiation
      1. How Does Radiation Affect Cells?
      2. Health Effects of Radiation
   D. Minimizing the Risk

Objectives

After studying this chapter, the student should be able to:

1. Identify both *short-term* and *long-term goals* for energy development policies.
2. Outline the *nuclear fuel cycle* and argue the pros and cons of continued nuclear power development, including *breeder* reactors.
3. Summarize the potentials and drawbacks of *nuclear fusion, coal, oil, natural gas,* and *synthetic fuels* as energy sources suitable for long-term reliance.
4. Distinguish *passive solar, active solar,* and *photovoltaics.*
5. Cite the major advantages and disadvantages of *solar energy* relative to other energy sources under consideration.
6. Assess the potential for each of the following renewable energy sources: *biomass, hydroelectricity, geothermal,* and *hydrogen.*
7. Outline the advantages and disadvantages of, and techniques available for, making *conservation* the cornerstone of any new energy policy.
8. Identify several major features of a sustainable energy system.
9. Argue the desirability of shifting to a *sustainable energy system.*
10. Identify the three types of *nuclear radiation,* their primary sources, and their relative threats to human health.

Lecture Notes

I. ESTABLISHING A SHOPPING LIST
   • Serious errors were made by haphazard and misguided energy development in the absence of a well-thought *plan.*
   • An appropriate energy plan will concern itself with both energy *supply* and energy *efficiency.*
   • *Short-term* goals should include *improving efficiency* and *replacing petroleum* with other fuels.
   • *Intermediate-term* goals are to find replacements for *natural gas.*
   • *Long-term* goals involve *replacing coal* with other substitutes.

II. NONRENEWABLE ENERGY SOURCES

   A. Nuclear Fission
      • *Nuclear fission* produces heat by splitting fissile atoms such as U-235.
      1. Nuclear Power: Pros and Cons.
         • Nuclear power does *not* contribute to the *greenhouse effect* or *acid rain.*
         • It requires less *surface mining* and has lower fuel *transportation costs* and *impacts* than does coal.

- Nuclear power has at least a dozen *unique disadvantages*, some of which seriously threaten its viability.
  2. Reactor Safety
     - Attempts, such as the *Rasmussen Report*, to statistically assess nuclear power risks are fraught with difficulties and largely discredited today.
     - *Variables*, including *human error, terrorism*, and *sabotage* make nuclear reactor safety assessment difficult.
  3. Waste Disposal
     - *Radioactive wastes* are generated at several points in the fuel cycle; these wastes must be isolated for thousands of years.
     - *Disposal techniques* and *repositories* for high-level radioactive wastes have not yet been developed, despite the continued production of such wastes.
  4. Social Acceptability and Cost
     - When all planning, construction, licensing, operating, maintenance, and decommissioning costs are factored in, nuclear power is our most *expensive* energy source today.
     - *High costs, safety concerns*, and *mismanagement* have combined to lower the social acceptability of nuclear power relative to other energy sources.
  5. Proliferation of Nuclear Weapons
     - The link between *nuclear power* and *nuclear bombs* is well-established.
  6. Breeder Reactors
     - *Breeders* convert an abundant material (U-238) into *plutonium*, which can then be extracted to fuel other reactors; thus, breeders can theoretically multiply our nuclear fuel supply.
     - *Drawbacks* to breeder programs include *cost, safety concerns*, and *plutonium's toxicity* and desirability for nuclear *weapons* and terrorist *explosives*.

B. Nuclear Fusion
    - *Nuclear fusion* involves *combining* nuclei of light elements.
    - Numerous *technical problems* related to the operating design and reactants/products will delay commercial feasibility by several decades.

C. Coal
    - Despite its abundance and low cost, *coal* is environmentally damaging at every stage of the fuel cycle, and thus its overall desirability is relatively low.

D. Natural Gas
    - While relatively *clean* to extract and burn, its *limited abundance* diminishes its potential to alleviate future energy shortages.

E. Synthetic Fuels
    1. Oil Shale
       - Oil shale contains *kerogen* which can be heated to *shale oil* and refined into petroleum-like products.
       - Though *abundant* and *versatile*, shale oil is *expensive, inefficient*, and causes extreme *environmental damage* from mining and refining.
    2. Tar Sands
       - *Bitumen* in tar sands can be refined into petroleum substitutes; however, it is *economically* and *environmentally costly*, and supplies are limited.

3. Coal Gasification and Liquefaction
   * *Costs, air* and *water pollution,* and *net energy inefficiency* make coal gasification and liquefaction low-priority energy forms.

III. RENEWABLE ENERGY RESOURCES

A. Solar Energy
   1. Pros and Cons of Solar Energy
      * *Solar energy* is our most flexible and widely available, low-impact and nondepletable energy source.
      * *Free fuel* and *low maintenance costs* make solar economically appealing to forward-looking homeowners.
      * *Limitations* include solar's *intermittency* and resulting need for storage or back-up systems.
   2. Passive Solar Heating
      * This approach is to *design buildings* which passively utilize the sun's energy for space heating and lighting.
   3. Active Solar
      * These systems effectively and efficiently *heat* and *cool* air and/or water for residential and commercial buildings.
   4. Photovoltaics
      * *Solar cells* can generate *electricity* from sunlight; these are especially useful today in situations where other fuels are expensive or impractical.

B. Wind
   * The potential for *wind-generated electricity, heat,* and other *direct applications* is enormous.
   * *Wind* energy has most of the same advantages and disadvantages as solar energy.

C. Biomass
   * Energy from organic matter of plants, *biomass,* is significant in many parts of the world today, and can become more so in the U.S. if given a push by the government.
   * *Drawbacks* include increased competition between people for *food* and *energy* supplies if more resources are devoted to fuel rather than food farms.

D. Hydroelectric Power
   * This energy source is *renewable,* relatively *non-polluting,* and *inexpensive,* yet creation and maintenance of large dams and reservoirs has severe localized ecological impacts.

E. Geothermal Energy
   * *Hydrothermal convection, geopressure,* and *hot-rock-zones* are geothermal resources which are renewable and fairly clean but which have limited potential for future use.

F. Hydrogen Fuel
   * Made from splitting water molecules, *hydrogen gas* is renewable, low-polluting, and versatile; however, its *low net-energy yield* must be improved in order to justify widespread development.

G. The Renewable Energy Potential
   * Studies show that *renewable energy* makes up the bulk of *total* and *accessible* energy resources worldwide.
   * *Economics* and *convention,* both heavily influenced by government subsidies, give nonrenewable fuels the advantage today.

IV. CONSERVATION
- This must be a *top priority* in any energy program we adopt.
- *Conservation* saves *money, resources, pollution*, and is available now for large-scale implementation.
- Conservation techniques include *increasing efficiency* of fuel use, *cogeneration*, better *technology* in buildings, appliances, and industrial processes, and *lifestyle changes* which reduce personal energy consumption.
- *Incentives* for implementing existing conservation techniques and developing more include *taxes*, government-mandated *efficiency standards, pricing*, and *least-cost planning*.

V. BUILDING A SUSTAINABLE ENERGY SYSTEM
- Any system whose goal is *long-term sustainability* must rely almost exclusively on *renewable energy sources*.

A. Shifting to a Sustainable Transportation System
- *Transportation* consumes 30% of the energy used in the U.S.
1. Improving Efficiency
- *Increased mileage* in new cars can stretch our petroleum supplies.
2. From Road to Rails and Buses
- *Mass transit* can replace much of the use of autos if made available to most people.
- *Bicycles* can be effective adjuncts to an efficient transportation system.
3. Economic Changes Accompanying a Shift to Mass Transit
- *Transportation system changes* will have major *economic impacts*; these can be minimized with proper planning.

VI. CHAPTER SUPPLEMENT. RADIATION POLLUTION
- *Radionuclides* naturally emit radiation in one of three forms: *alpha particles, beta particles*, or *gamma rays; X rays* are not naturally occurring.
- *Ionizing radiation* in any of the above forms damages living tissues by creating charged atoms, *ions*, which are highly reactive.

A. How Is Radiation Measured?
- *Radiation exposure* in humans is measured in *RADs*, or radiation absorbed doses, an expression of energy amounts released in tissue.
- *Rems* are units of radiation exposure measurement which take into account tissue damage caused by that type of radiation.

B. Sources of Radiation
1. Natural Sources
- These include *air, water, soil*, and *atmospheric* sources of radiation.
- Over *80%* of our radiation exposure is from *natural sources*.
2. Anthropogenic Sources
- These include *medical* exposure, *nuclear weapons* and *energy, TV sets* and some *watches*, and *air travel*.

C. Effects of Radiation
1. How Does Radiation Affect Cells?
- *Radiation damages* cells and tissues primarily through its *ionizing effects*, creating highly reactive molecules which can oxidize or otherwise disrupt normal cellular processes.

2. Health Effects of Radiation
   - Though *variable* due to a number of factors, *health effects of radiation* include *death, radiation sickness*, and a host of *delayed effects*, including cancer and sterility, from *high-level* doses.
   - *Low-level* doses are thought to increase *cancer* and *leukemia* rates, *genetic defects*, increase *aging*, and perhaps *suppress* natural *immunity*.

D. Minimizing the Risk
   - Taking steps to *eliminate unnecessary* and *reduce necessary medical X rays* will minimize one's risk from anthropogenic radiation exposure.

Case Study

Is Nuclear Power the Answer to Global Warming?

It's an exemplary promo plan. The music ebbs and flows in the background; the narrator's voice massages his unseen audience. The topic is power without fear. General Atomics, we are told, has a new process for generating electricity, a process that will satisfy the public, the utilities, and the investment community. The product -- the high-temperature, gas-cooled nuclear reactor -- may sound technical and recondite, but it lays claim to some comforting and simple adjectives: safe, reliable, and cost-effective.

1953? No, 1989. The General Atomics nuclear reactor is just one of several so-called advanced models emerging in the energy spotlight as concern over global warming increases. To more and more policymakers, the newly designed reactors are feasible alternatives to coal, oil, and natural gas power plants, all of which emit carbon dioxide (CO_2), one of the primary culprits behind the greenhouse effect.

Somewhat fewer people see the reactors as preferable to the large, expensive, and cumbersome water-cooled models that, despite their faults, have so far been the United States' reactors of choice. With sufficient federal support, the gas-cooled version could, its sponsors speculate, be in the vanguard of a second generation of nuclear reactors. Even some members of Congress who have historically made themselves at home in the environmentalist camp are tempted by the new reactors, saying that in light of the greenhouse effect, it's time to reevaluate nuclear power.

Any such appraisal must begin with an understanding of the contribution nuclear reactors could reasonably make toward reducing greenhouse gas emissions. Obviously, to the extent that a nuclear plant is built instead of, or as a replacement for, an existing fossil-fuel plant, CO_2 emissions will be reduced. If it were possible to replace all U.S. fossil-fuel-burning plants with nuclear facilities, total CO_2 emissions would be reduced by 28 percent nationwide. (This estimate does not reflect the undetermined but possibly significant amount of fossil fuels used -- and CO_2 emitted -- during the construction and operation of a nuclear plant.) But CO_2 is not the only malefactor. Taking into account the methane, chlorofluorocarbons, and other trace gases that are also warming the planet, nuclear power could offset only 14 percent of all U.S. greenhouse gas emissions.

Nuclear power's contribution dwindles as the territory expands. Replacing all U.S. fossil-fuel plants with nuclear reactors would reduce global greenhouse gas emissions by about 4 percent. And, as the use of fossil fuels grows in the Third World, the figure drops further.

Assuming a full-scale nuclear mobilization were nonetheless desirable, and assuming no inflation in the 1987 average cost of constructing a nuclear reactor in the United States, replacing the nation's fossil-fuel-generated electricity with nuclear-generated electricity would cost $1.2 trillion. And, if nuclear advocates are not yet deterred, there's one more consideration: According to analyst Bill Keepin of the Rocky Mountain Institute, to replace coal-burning power plants, nuclear capacity would have to increase "at the staggering rate of one large nuclear plant every 1.6 days for the next 38 years" in a high-growth scenario and every 2.4 days in a medium-growth scenario. Utility analyst Charles Komanoff adds that nuclear reactors would have to come on-line worldwide at the rate of eight per week to displace just half the CO_2 emissions of fossil-fuel plants over the next 35 years.

Formidable as these numbers are, they do not daunt the nuclear industry. In press releases and congressional testimony, industry representatives repeatedly tout nuclear as CO_2- free. And when critics pull out the numbers showing nuclear's limited potential, industry spokespersons hold up the red flag of global warming. Indeed, one of the major pieces of federal legislation addressing the greenhouse effect, introduced by Sen. Timothy Wirth (D-Colo.), proposes, among other things, spending $500 million to demonstrate the feasibility of advanced reactors. Wirth, considered one of the more environmentally minded members of Congress, has said that Americans must get over their "nuclear measles" and that "environmentalists will come around. They can't help but come around."

Perhaps more to the point is whether, given its technical, financial, and regulatory difficulties, nuclear power itself can come around. No new reactors have been ordered in the United States since 1978, and all those ordered between 1974 and 1978 have been canceled. The problems at the 111 licensed civilian reactors make it unlikely that any new ones will be ordered soon. Many facilities are aging prematurely, their reactor vessels becoming "embrittled" -- that is, weakened from continuous exposure to radiation. Despite modifications, the eight reactors designed by Babcock & Wilcox (manufacturers of the reactors at Three Mile Island) are still trouble-prone, while the containment systems for 24 operating General Electric reactors are, according to a study sponsored by the Nuclear Regulatory Commission (NRC), likely to fail in the event of a major accident.

After more than three decades of commercial operation, nuclear power has yet to prove itself safe. During the last decade, U.S. nuclear utilities have reported nearly 30,000 mishaps at their plants, including the partial meltdown in 1979 at Three Mile Island and several close calls since then.

The NRC, the agency charged with oversight of the nation's nuclear power plants, inspires little confidence. Congressional hearings have focused on the NRC's "coziness" with the industry it regulates: Rule changes often benefit the industry; safety procedures are haphazardly enforced; and, in general, the agency is unwilling to require safety improvements that might be expensive for a utility to implement. The NRC is, in short, reluctant to take any action that might imply that all is not quiet on the nuclear front.

The present aside, no one yet knows what to do with a reactor once it has reached the end of its useful life. Nor has a politically and technologically trustworthy decision been made regarding nuclear waste. Last year [1988] Congress decided to send the nation's high-level nuclear waste to an underground repository to be built below Yucca Mountain, Nevada, but controversy over that choice has delayed exploratory work, and few observers expect Yucca Mountain to open its doors on schedule in 2003.

Advocates of advanced reactors believe that the new design of their machines will diminish concerns about nuclear safety and, by extension, about regulation. Senator Wirth's interest in nuclear power as part of any greenhouse solution is predicated on the belief that an "inherently safe" reactor can in fact be built. Suddenly, the term "inherently safe" is everywhere. Sometimes the somewhat less colorful term "passively safe" is used; one advanced-reactor design is even named PIUS -- Passive Inherent Ultimate Safe.

For those who believe nuclear's woes are a result of bad P.R. and an irrationally fearful public, the new and improved lingo may hold a certain attraction. But Robert Pollard, a former safety engineer with the NRC who now works with the Union of Concerned Scientists, points out that fissioning atoms is, if anything, inherently dangerous. You can compensate for that and perhaps make it acceptable to the public, he says, but you can't make it inherently safe. Many in the nuclear industry itself are also uncomfortable with the terminology. "The connotation of the term is misleading," says Carl Goldstein of the U.S. Committee on Energy Awareness, a nuclear-industry trade group. "We absolutely cannot tell the public that something is inherently safe." Goldstein says a significant number of his organization's members feel likewise.

Semantics aside, how advanced are the advanced reactors? While there have been the sorts of improvements in circuitry, piping, and so forth that one would expect in any technology, the basic advance is in the method of cooling the reactor core. All nuclear reactors must have a system for cooling the core in case of an accident, to avoid melting the reactor fuel and releasing radioactivity into the environment. The new designs all move away from the conventional "active" pumping systems laden with moving parts to "passive" systems that rely to a greater extent on natural forces such as gravity.

The advanced reactors sound impressive. Not only are they supposed to be safer, they'll be smaller and possibly less expensive than conventional nuclear plants. There's just one problem: Most exist only on paper. Karl Stahlkopf, who directs advanced-reactor research at the Electric Power Research Institute in Palo Alto, California, notes that while portions of the designs do exist at some plants in the United States and overseas, "We're looking well into the next decade before any of these are certified" by the NRC.

General Atomics disagrees. The company believes that the basic concept of the high-temperature, gas-cooled reactor (HTGR) has already been proved and that only the specifics need to be demonstrated. The company also says that while it is confident of the HTGR's cost-effectiveness, it does need several hundred million dollars from the federal government to prove this fact. William Moomaw, director of the World Resources Institute's climate and energy program, questions the wisdom of such a subsidy: "With an industry as mature as the nuclear industry, shouldn't it be paying for this itself?" Pollard of the Union of Concerned Scientists concurs: "If you can't find private investors, that should tell you something."

Ultimately, the safety assurances of General Atomics and others melt away when the companies are pressed on the issue of accident liability. The Price-Anderson Act, renewed by Congress last year, protects the nuclear utilities -- and, by extension, the reactor manufacturers -- by placing a dollar limit on the liability they would face in the event of a nuclear accident. Is the industry willing to forgo that coverage and accept financial liability for an accident at one of their "inherently safe" reactors? "No," says Tom Johnston, executive consultant to General Atomics. But if the reactors will be so safe, then why not? "People in this business," Johnston explains, "are very, very conservative."

Despite attempts by the nuclear industry to characterize environmentalists as being "split" on the question of a nuclear revival, the environmental community generally agrees that nuclear power need not play a role in any comprehensive response to global warming.

The best CO_2-free "source" is energy efficiency. Analyses conducted at Princeton University and the Lawrence Berkeley Laboratory show that developed countries could cut per capita energy demand by as much as 50 percent over the next 20 to 30 years and still maintain current rates of industrial expansion and economic growth. Although improvements in energy efficiency will require capital investment, Rocky Mountain Institute's Keepin estimates that each dollar put into efficiency displaces seven times more CO_2 than a dollar spent on nuclear power. The United States in particular has a long way to go to improve its energy efficiency. Last summer, the World Resources Institute's Moomaw testified before the Senate that "Japan produces a dollar of GNP, or the equivalent in yen, while using about half of the energy" that Americans use.

After efficiency, renewable sources of energy such as solar, wind, and geothermal power are the next-best energy investment. According to the Department of Energy, renewable resources constitute one of the nation's largest energy reserves -- more than five times the energy potential embedded in the country's coal reserves -- and could meet up to 80 percent of America's projected energy needs in 2010.

Slowing the warming of our planet will be costly no matter what steps are taken. It will involve international cooperation to stop deforestation, increase tree planting, eliminate chlorofluorocarbon emissions, and reduce fossil-fuel combustion in transportation, industry, residences, and power plants. But taking no action at all would end up being even more costly and would mean a tripling of CO_2 emissions over the next 50 years. Investments in energy efficiency will not only reverse that, but will free capital for reforestation and other greenhouse-mitigating activities.

Nonetheless, nuclear power still has the upper hand over energy efficiency in at least two respects, according to David Hawkins, an attorney with the Natural Resources Defense Council. "We're dealing with human beings, whose psychology tends to be dominated by what appears to be the easiest fix. Somehow, we must focus on harder-to-grasp issues like energy efficiency. It's difficult, for we're sitting at the table with people who say, 'Here, we'll sell you the answer, in a technological box.'"

Hawkins points out that in addition to holding this psychological advantage, the nuclear industry tends to dominate the agenda of energy policymakers. "It's like going to a dinner party with Henry Kissinger," he says. "Everyone is going to pay attention to him, even if someone else has something better to say."

From "Reactors Redux" by Michael Philips, *Sierra*, March/April 1989.

Critical Thinking Problems

1. Assuming we all agree that a shift to a sustainable energy system is desirable, and recognizing that such a shift will have significant economic repercussions, how do we make the shift without unjustly disadvantaging certain groups, such as coal miners and auto workers? Or, must we simply accept the idea that some individuals' interests must be sacrificed for the good of society?

2. Are there strong ethical arguments against nuclear power? If so, what duties do they rest on? Consider the entire fuel cycle and take into account not only the interests of people alive today but also of those yet to be born.

3. Does increasing energy consumption necessarily benefit an economy and stimulate employment? Must we choose between a healthy economy and a sustainable energy future?

Test Questions

Multiple Choice. Each of the following questions has one correct answer. Circle the letter corresponding to the choice you think best answers the question.

B   1.   Nuclear fission reactors:

      a.   are fueled today by plutonium.
      b.   contain fissionable (fissile) uranium in fuel rods.
      c.   are most often cooled by liquid sodium.
      d.   rely on the fission of helium nuclei.

A   2.   Which of the following is true?

      a.   Uranium-235 emits neutrons naturally.
      b.   Uranium-235 atoms fuse to form plutonium in a fusion reactor.
      c.   Uranium-235 is a renewable resource.
      d.   Uranium-235 is the nonfissile form of uranium.

C   3.   Control rods in a fission reactor:

      a.   contain uranium.
      b.   release neutrons into the uranium fuel.
      c.   contain neutron-absorbing materials.
      d.   when completely lowered, allow the reactor to operate at full speed.

B   4.   Breeder reactors:

      a.   use uranium-235 as a fuel.
      b.   produce plutonium-239, which can be used as fuel in other reactors.
      c.   are well established and economical.
      d.   begin making a surplus of fuel shortly after they are put into operation.
      e.   a & c
      e.   b & d

D   5.   Most fission reactors in operation today:

      a.   are of the fast breeder variety.
      b.   are cooled by liquid sodium.
      c.   use plutionium-239 fuel.
      d.   none of the above

C   6.   Fusion reactors:

      a.   unite two helium nuclei to produce energy.
      b.   produce less energy per gram of fuel than fission but pose a lower risk.
      c.   could provide a virtually inexhaustible supply of energy but so far have proved difficult to contain and costly to tap.
      d.   all of the above

D 7. Oil shale:

    a. is a fine-grained sedimentary rock that contains an insoluble organic material called kerogen.
    b. when heated, releases a thick liquid called shale oil.
    c. deposits lie under much of the continental United States, but the richest deposits are found in the West.
    d. all of the above

A 8. Coal gasification:

    a. is the treatment of coal with heat, oxygen, and hydrogen to produce combustible gas.
    b. requires only small amounts of water and thus can be easily carried out in more arid climates.
    c. produces few pollutants and is therefore a good way to replace natural gas supplies.
    e. a & b
    f. b & c

A 9. Coal liquefaction:

    a. produces a synthetic oil from coal.
    b. is a relatively clean process, producing few air and water pollutants and requiring virtually no energy input.
    c. could provide a synthetic natural gas needed to replace falling supplies of natural gas.
    d. none of the above

C 10. Which of the following is true regarding solar energy?

    a. Over their lifetime, solar systems rarely pay back the energy needed to construct them.
    b. Solar energy is a high-quality energy source.
    c. Solar energy could be used to provide much of our energy for space heating.
    d. Solar energy is an experimental form of energy waiting for major technological breakthroughs before it is possible to implement.

A 11. Passive solar energy:

    a. captures sunlight energy in buildings for space heating.
    b. requires panels to collect sunlight energy and heat water.
    c. is used primarily to heat water.
    d. produces electricity.

E 12. Photovoltaics:

    a. could find their first major market in developing countries that need decentralized energy sources for rural villages.
    b. Consist of thin layers of silicon or other materials that emit electrons when struck by sunlight.
    c. are used to power most U.S. satellites.
    d. are not yet economically competitive with conventional electrical production.
    e. all of the above

E   13. Biomass:

    a. could provide boundless energy supplies.
    b. can be burned or converted to liquid and gaseous fuels.
    c. provides about 19% of the United States' energy needs.
    d. is an indirect form of solar energy.
    e. b & d
    f. a & c

D   14. Conservation:

    a. has been fully exploited in this country.
    b. is a good idea but only when energy prices are high.
    c. saves little money and is therefore not worth the investment.
    d. is the most cost-effective energy source available.
    e. a & b
    f. c & d

Fill in the Blank. For each of the following questions, fill in the blank with the appropriate word or phrase.

1.   The products of nuclear fission are called _____ nuclei.

2.   The reactor vessel is surrounded by a thick cement shell called the reactor _____ building.

3.   The waste from a uranium mill is called _____ _____.

4.   _____ confinement is a technique where a fusion fuel is suspended by a magnetic field.

5.   Heating fractured oil shale in the ground is called ____ _____ _____.

6.   Runaway chain reactions in a nuclear reactor would cause a core _____.

7.   Brick walls and cement underlying tile floors store heat in passive solar homes and are generally referred to as _____ mass.

8.   _____ _____ zones are regions where magma heats rock containing large amounts of groundwater.

9.   Hydrogen is generated by heating water in the presence of a _____, a chemical that facilitates the breakdown of water and remains unchanged in the process.

10.   Heat moves directly through walls and ceilings of homes. This loss is called _____.

Answers: 1. daughter   2. containment   3. mill tailings   e. Magnetic   5. in situ retorting
6. meltdown   7. thermal   8. Hydrothermal convection   9. catalyst   10. conduction

Short Essay. Write a 250-300 word essay to answer each of the following questions.

1. Discuss the pros and cons of nuclear energy.

2. How does a breeder reactor work? How is it different from the more conventional fission reactors?

3. Describe the pros and cons of oil shale development.

4. Fusion energy has many promises, but the technical problems and cost probably will never make it a good energy source. Defend or refute this statement.

5. Describe coal gasification and liquefaction.

6. Defend or refute this statement: Hydroelectric power is an immense, untapped energy resource in the U.S. and could provide an enormous amount of energy.

7. Describe the three major ways geothermal energy can be tapped.

8. Describe major ways we could cut back on energy consumption in the U.S.

9. Define the term "passive solar heating" and describe a typical passive solar system.

10. Discuss the advantages and disadvantages of wind power.

Chapter Supplement. Radiation Pollution

Fill in the Blank. For each of the following questions, fill in the blank with the appropriate word or phrase.

1. Atoms of the same element differ in the number of neutrons they contain; these different forms are called _____.

2. Radioactive nuclei are called _____.

3. _____ _____ are positively charged particles emitted from radioactive nuclei.

4. The unit of measure that takes into account the amount of energy that is deposited in tissue struck by radiation is called the _____.

5. The rate of energy loss for radiation as it travels through a tissue is called the _____ _____ _____.

Answers: 1. isotopes   2. radionuclides   3. Alpha particles   4. rad   5. linear energy transfer

Short Essay. Write a 250-300 word essay to answer each of the following questions.

1. What is radiation and where does it come from?

2. How does radiation damage cells?

3. Describe the symptoms of high-level radiation.

Suggested Readings and Resource Materials

Stobaugh, R. and D. Yergin, Eds. (1979). *Energy Future.* New York: Random House. A classic treatise by the Energy Project of the Harvard Business School on energy, economics, and the future.

Brown, Lester. *Food or Fuel: New Competition for the World's Cropland.* Washington, DC: WorldWatch Institute.

Flavin, Christopher. *Energy and Architecture: The Solar and Conservation Potential.* Washington, DC: WorldWatch Institute.

Flavin, Christopher. *Electricity From Sunlight: The Future of Photovoltaics.* Washington, DC: WorldWatch Institute.

Goldemburg et al. (1987). *Energy for a Sustainable World.* Washington, DC: World Resources Institute. Explores in detail the technological opportunities for using energy more efficiently.

Videos: For ordering information, see Film/Video Index.

Chernobyl and Three Mile Island. A discussion by leading Soviet and American scientists. Contact The Video Project.

Chernobyl: Chronicle of Difficult Weeks. Filmed by the first film crew to enter the area after the accident. Contact The Video Project.

A Question of Power. An in-depth chronicle of the struggles over California's Diablo Canyon nuclear plant. Contact The Video Project.

Films for the Humanities & Sciences has several films on energy sources for the future, including: *Energy Alternatives: Fusion; Energy Alternatives: Solar; Green Energy; Chernobyl: A Taste of Wormwood*; and, *Acceptable Risks?* Contact Films for the Humanities & Sciences.

CHAPTER 13

THE EARTH AND ITS MINERAL RESOURCES

Outline

I. THE EARTH AND ITS RICHES
   A. A Rocky Beginning
   B. The Movements of Continents

II. MINERAL RESOURCES AND SOCIETY
   A. Who Consumes the World's Minerals?
   B. Growing Interdependence and Global Tensions
   C. Will There Be Enough?

III. MEETING FUTURE NEEDS
   A. Can We Expand Our Reserves?
      1. Rising Prices, Rising Supplies
      2. Using Technology to Expand Reserves
      3. Factors that Reduce Supplies
      4. Rising Energy Costs: A Key Factor
      5. Environmental Costs
      6. Minerals From Outer Space and the Sea
   B. Can We Find Substitutes?
   C. Can Recycling Stretch Our Supplies?
      1. Recycling: Only a Partial Answer
   D. Can Conservation Stretch Our Supplies?
      1. Some Suggested Personal Actions

Objectives

After studying this chapter, the student should be able to:

1. Describe the *rock cycle* and relate its implications for mineral supply limitations.
2. Identify the major *importers* of minerals and discuss the political and economic vulnerability of importers due to this dependence.
3. Argue pro and con the idea that mineral resources are *infinite*, either on this planet or in the universe.

Lecture Notes

I. THE EARTH AND ITS RICHES

   A. A Rocky Beginning
      • As the earth's crust cooled, *mineral deposits* were formed.

- Geological processes often *concentrate* minerals in *igneous rocks.*
- An *ore* is a mineral deposit which can be economically *mined* or *refined.*

B. The Movements of Continents
   - The term *rock cycle* describes the continuous *movement* of the earth's crust.
   - The earth's crust is composed of *layers* and is broken into several *tectonic plates.*
   - These plates were once part of a giant continent, *Pangea.*
   - The nature and location of critical parts of the rock cycle make mineral ore deposits essentially *finite.*

II. MINERAL RESOURCES AND SOCIETY

A. Who Consumes the World's Minerals?
   - The *developed nations* consume a disproportionately large amount of the minerals marketed today.

B. Growing Interdependence and Global Tensions
   - Large developed nations heavily depend on mineral *imports*; this dependence creates *vulnerability* because of political and economic instability of the exporting nations.

C. Will There Be Enough?
   - Concerns about long-term supplies of important minerals and rates of use are legitimate.

III. MEETING FUTURE NEEDS

A. Can We Expand Our Reserves?
   - *Short-term expansion* is feasible, whereas *long-term expansion* is problematic.
   1. Rising Prices, Rising Supplies
      - The laws of *supply and demand* indicate that we can expand supplies by recovering less accessible reserves as price increases make this economically feasible.
      - In the *long run*, though, increased demand and diminishing supply must ultimately *deplete* a nonrenewable mineral resource.
   2. Using Technology to Expand Reserves
      - While helpful in increasing extraction efficiency, *technological advances* cannot make mineral resources infinite in supply.
   3. Factors That Reduce Supplies
      - Many factors, including *energy* and *environmental constraints*, can inhibit production and expansion of mineral reserves.
   4. Rising Energy Costs: A Key Factor
      - There are *economic limits* which will be reached before the *physical limits* of mineral supplies are neared.
   5. Environmental Costs
      - *Disturbance* and *pollution* from mining/refining lower-grade deposits will increase costs and speed economic depletion of many minerals.
   6. Minerals From Outer Space and the Sea
      - Untapped mineral deposits await us in *outer space, Antarctica*, and the *oceans* -- but only with enormous environmental damage, cost, effort, and risk.

B. Can We Find Substitutes?
- While *substitutes* undoubtedly can be found for some depleted minerals, they may themselves be limited; and, in any case, recycling and conserving are preferable to reliance on technological fixes.

C. Can Recycling Stretch Our Supplies?
- *Recycling* can dramatically slow our consumption of virgin ores by increasing a minerals's *residence time*.
  1. Recycling: Only a Partial Answer
     - Since recycling can never reach 100% for any mineral, it cannot be *the* solution to mineral depletion.

D. Can Conservation Stretch Our Supplies?
- *Conservation* can extend the lifetimes of many valuable mineral supplies.
  1. Some Suggested Personal Actions
     - *Careful* and *reduced buying*, adopting a *low-impact lifestyle*, and *supporting legislation* aimed at increasing conservation and recycling will help initiate society-wide changes necessary to head off mineral depletion.

Critical Thinking Problems

1. Suppose we find a way to economically mine a strategic mineral to physical depletion of ore reserves. Considering that future generations may also have a need for that material, are we morally justified in depleting it to satisfy demand today? If not, how many future generations should we save some for?

2. If we have no alternative but to turn to Antarctica, the oceans, and outer space to supply us needed minerals, what does this say about human population and global carrying capacity?

3. Imagine that we discover a "mineral genie" who agrees to give us limitless reserves of all important minerals. Can you think of any reasons to reduce demand and recycle minerals *anyway*?

Test Questions

Multiple Choice. Each of the following questions has one correct answer. Circle the letter corresponding to the choice you think best answers the question.

D 1. Nonfuel minerals:

   a. are consumed primarily by the developing nations.
   b. decrease in value as they are processed and incorporated into goods.
   c. are mined primarily in the developed nations.
   d. none of the above
   e. all of the above

F   2.   Expanding nonfuel mineral reserves often takes place as prices rise:

a. because mining companies often use the increased revenues to find new deposits.
b. because increased prices make it possible to move reserves too costly to mine into the economic reserve category.
c. because new technologies can be developed to mine lower grade ores.
d. a & b
e. b & c
f. a, b, & c

A   3.   Which of the following factors might decrease nonfuel mineral reserves?

a. rising energy costs
b. falling labor costs
c. relaxation of environmental controls
d. falling interest rates

C   4.   Which of the following best summarizes the position of the limitist?

a. Mineral reserves will continue to expand.
b. Mineral reserves are infinite in comparison to demand.
c. Mineral reserves are finite and will someday be exhausted.
d. Mineral reserves can continue to expand as long as prices rise.

C   5.   Recycling:

a. saves very little energy.
b. is practiced widely through the United States.
c. can drastically slow down the depletion of minerals but will not stop it entirely.
d. a & b
e. b & c

Fill in the Blank. For each of the following questions, fill in the blank with the appropriate word or phrase.

1.   Granite and basalt are _____ rocks formed when molten minerals cool.

2.   Shale and sandstone are _____ rocks formed from the eroded particles of other types of rock.

3.   A concentrated deposit of minerals that can be mined and refined economically is called an _____.

4.   The earth's crust is broken into large plates called _____ plates.

5.   The zone where one plate is pushed under another is called a _____ zone.

6.   _____ nodules are abundant on the floor of the Pacific ocean and may provide much-needed minerals for future generations.

7.   Scientists use the term _____ to denote disorder.

106

8. The time a mineral remains in use in society is called its _____ time.

9. The first state to pass a bottle bill was _____.

10. _____ is often the cheapest and easiest way to stretch mineral supplies.

Answers: 1. igneous 2. sedimentary 3. ore 4. tectonic 5. subduction 6. Manganese
7. entropy 8. residence 9. Oregon 10. Conservation

Short Essay. Write a 250-300 word essay to answer each of the following questions.

1. Debate the statement: Substitution has been a useful strategy in the past when a resource has become economically depleted, and it will continue to be a valuable weapon in the future.

2. Outline a mineral plan which seeks to satisfy our long-term mineral needs. What are the key elements of your plan? How would you go about implementing this plan?

Suggested Readings and Resource Materials

Westing, Arthur (1986). *Global Resources and International Conflict*. New York: Oxford University Press. Excellent overview and analysis.

Frosch, R. A. and N. E. Gallopoulos. "Strategies for Manufacturing" in *Scientific American*, September 1989, pp. 136-143. Examines ways to maintain the industrial way of life without exhausting resources.

Videos: For ordering information, see Film/Video Index.

Strip Mining: Energy, Environment, and Economics. Details the history and consequences of surface mining coal; relevant to discussions about mining/mineral extraction in general. Contact Appalshop Films.

CHAPTER 14

TOXIC SUBSTANCES:
PRINCIPLES AND PRACTICALITIES

Outline

I. PRINCIPLES OF TOXICOLOGY
    A. Biological Effects of Toxins
        1. Acute Effects
        2. Chronic Effects
        3. Cancer
        4. Mutations
        5. Birth Defects
        6. Reproductive Toxicity
    B. How Do Toxins Work?
    C. Factors Affecting the Toxicity of Chemicals
        1. Dose and Duration
        2. Biological Activity
        3. Age
        4. Health Status
        5. Synergy and Antagonism
    D. Bioconcentration and Biological Magnification

II. THE ROOTS OF CONTROVERSY

III. CONTROLLING TOXIC SUBSTANCES
    A. Federal Control
    B. Market Incentives to Control Toxic Chemicals

IV. DETERMINING THE RISKS
    A. Risks and Hazards: Overlapping Boundaries
    B. Risk Assessment
    C. Risk Management: Decisions About Risk Acceptability
        1. Decisions, Decisions
        2. Actual Versus Perceived Risk
    D. The Final Standard: Ethics
        1. Prioritizing Values
        2. Space-Time Values
        3. Building the Future

V. CHAPTER SUPPLEMENT. GLOBAL LEAD POLLUTION
    A. Sources of Lead
    B. Effects of High-Level Exposure
    C. Effects of Low-Level Exposure
    D. Controls on Lead

Objectives

After studying this chapter, the student should be able to:

1. Discuss the acute and chronic *biological effects* of toxins.
2. Define the terms *toxin, carcinogen, mutagen,* and *teratogen* and give several examples of each.
3. List the three ways toxins are known to disrupt cellular metabolism.
4. Cite several factors which affect the *toxicity* of chemicals.
5. Assess the difficulties in *extrapolating* human health risk data from animal test data.
6. Give an example of a *federal program* and a *marketing incentive program* designed to control toxins.
7. Weigh the various factors which enter into *risk assessment* and the resulting decisions concerning *risk management*.
8. Identify the role of *values* in shaping our attitudes towards environmental risks.
9. Discuss the major sources and health effects of *lead* in the environment and cite ways in which human exposure can be reduced.

Lecture Notes

I. PRINCIPLES OF TOXICOLOGY
  - *60,000* chemical substances are used commercially in the U.S.
  - Of these, relatively few pose serious risks, yet those risks are substantial.
  - Due to economic and time constraints, only a small percentage of potentially harmful chemicals are tested for sub-acute toxicity.

  A. Biological Effects of Toxins
   - *Toxicology* is the study of the health effects of toxins; these effects are determined by the toxin's *chemical structure* and *concentration* and by the victim's *duration of exposure*.
   1. Acute Effects
     - These appear *shortly after exposure* and may be quite *severe*.
   2. Chronic Effects
     - These are *delayed* responses generally due to long-term, low-level exposure.
   3. Cancer
     - *Cancer* is an uncontrolled proliferation of cells, caused by one of a variety of agents or *carcinogens*.
     - *Environmental factors, food additives* and other products, and *occupational exposure* account for most cancers not due to smoking.
   4. Mutations
     - *Mutations* are alterations of the genetic material.
     - Agents which cause mutations are *mutagens*.
     - Mutations of germ-cells can be passed from one generation to the next.
   5. Birth Defects
     - These are *physical, biochemical,* or *functional* abnormalities.
     - Agents which cause birth defects are *teratogens*; their effects depend on *timing of exposure* and the *nature* of the teratogen.
   6. Reproductive Toxicity
     - Many drugs and environmental agents can interfere with reproduction; the study of these is *reproductive toxicology*.

  B. How Do Toxins Work:
   - *Toxins* disrupt cellular metabolism in a variety of ways.

C. Factors Affecting the Toxicity of Chemicals
   1. Dose and Duration
      * *Higher doses* and *longer exposures* tend to increase toxic effects.
      * The LD_{50} is the dose of a toxin lethal to 50% of the test animals.
   2. Biological Activity
      * *Biological activity* is a measure of a substance's *reactivity* in living systems.
   3. Age
      * *Younger organisms* are usually more sensitive to toxins than are adults.
   4. Health Status
      * *Genetic predispositions* and one's *lifestyle* may influence one's susceptibility to the effects of toxins.
   5. Synergy and Antagonism
      * Two or more toxic substances present together can alter the expected response. A *synergistic response* is one in which the results are *amplified*; an *antagonistic* response is one in which the effects are *negated*.

D. Bioconcentration and Biological Magnification
   * *Bioconcentration* is the accumulation of certain chemicals in the body.
   * *Biological magnification* is the buildup of chemicals through a food chain.

II. THE ROOTS OF CONTROVERSY
   * Physiological differences make it difficult to extrapolate results from lab animals to humans in *toxicity tests*.
   * Difficulty isolating the effects of any one agent and uncertainties resulting from high test doses further compound this difficulty.
   * *High doses* are necessary, though, to speed and make observable any toxic effects, and to exceed the agent's *threshold level* in lab animals.

III. CONTROLLING TOXIC SUBSTANCES

A. Federal Control
   * The *Toxic Substances Control Act* is intended to screen and regulate chemicals to minimize human health risk.
   * The Act requires *premanufacture notification, testing,* and *hazard minimization*.

B. Marketing Incentives to Control Toxic Chemicals
   * In California, a law requires manufacturers to either meet state-set standards for toxins or label their products accordingly, thus reducing the *marketability* of those products not in compliance.

IV. DETERMINING THE RISKS

A. Risks and Hazards: Overlapping Boundaries
   * *Risk* is a relative assessment of the threat posed by *anthropogenic* and *natural hazards*.

B. Risk Assessment
   * Through *hazard identification* and *risk estimation, risk assessment* seeks to help us understand and quantify risks in our lives.
   * Risk assessment is necessarily *imprecise* due to the nature of *probability* and *severity* estimates.

C. Risk Management: Decisions About Risk Acceptability
   - Since all activities involve some degree of *risk*, this is a *relative* term.
   - *Risk acceptability* is influenced by fear, perceived benefit, and perceived harm.
   1. Decisions, Decisions
      - Deciding which risks to accept in order to procure benefits involves *tradeoffs*.
      - *Cost/benefit* analysis is a popular decision-making tool, though it is impossible to accurately quantify all benefits and costs relevant to most risk decisions.
   2. Actual Versus Perceived Risk
      - When *actual* and *perceived risk* do not coincide, the result may be legislative *over-* or *underprotection*.

D. The Final Standard: Ethics
   - Ultimately, our *values* determine our attitudes with regard to environmental risks.
   1. Prioritizing Values
      - Our *values* must be *prioritized* in order for us to weigh and assess relative risks.
   2. Space-Time Values
      - Our values also reflect certain *spatial* and *temporal parameters* which influence our decision-making.
   3. Building the Future
      - It is incumbent upon us to build a future in which risks are realistically assessed and minimized and where, if errors are made, they are made on the side of *safety*.

V. CHAPTER SUPPLEMENT. GLOBAL LEAD POLLUTION

A. Sources of Lead
   - Lead is *versatile* and *widely used*; thus, human exposure from air, soil, and water is unavoidable.

B. Effects of High-Level Exposure
   - *High-level exposure* can cause a variety of *neurological, psychological,* and *physiological* problems.

C. Effects of Low-Level Exposure
   - These include varying degrees of *intellectual* and *emotional impairment*, especially in children.

D. Controls on Lead
   - The U.S. leads the world in legislative controls aimed at reducing average exposures to lead from airborne sources and food.

Case Study

Reducing the Need for Animal Testing

In 1933, Mrs. Brown applied an eyelash dye to her eyelashes in hopes of improving her appearance. For three months after this, she suffered constant pain until one day her corneas, the clear portion over the front of the eye, sloughed off. This tragic story was one of many presented before Congress by the U.S. Food and Drug Administration in the 1930s in its efforts to pass the Food, Drug, and Cosmetic Act.

Passed in 1938, the Act has no doubt helped avoid countless tragedies, but at the cost of thousands of laboratory animals each year. For instance, more than 100,000 rabbits are used each year in the United States to test potentially harmful cosmetic ingredients for eye irritation. Researchers squirt suspect chemicals into the eyes of rabbits, then watch them over a period of several days for signs of redness, blisters, bleeding, or blindness.

Upset with the pain and suffering animals must endure during such tests, animal activists are proposing the use of *in vitro* tests, tests on cell cultures that could replace many of the animal tests long used by the federal government and private research labs to determine toxicity.

Replacing animal tests for eye irritation seemed a crazy idea not many years ago. Today, however, *in vitro* testing has moved into the mainstream. At John Hopkins University, the Center for Alternatives to Animal Testing (CAAT), for example, is devoted to the study of alternative methods of testing.

Today, there are over 100 *in vitro* toxicology tests under development. Most of them use cell or tissue cultures. Many scientists, including those of leading cosmetic companies, agree that such tests offer substantial benefits. And several large companies, including Proctor and Gamble and Avon, have made a substantial commitment to eliminate animal testing.

The principal advantages of *in vitro* tests are several. First, they cost approximately one-tenth as much as animal tests. Second, the results can be much more precise. By studying changes in cell cultures, scientists can determine the exact influences chemical toxins have. The third benefit is that *in vitro* tests offer scientists an opportunity to learn more about the molecular mechanisms of toxicology.

Since membrane damage is one of the early signs of tissue toxicity, researchers are looking for ways to monitor these changes in cultures. The Neutral Red Uptake test, for example, assesses the uptake of a stain in human skin cells cultured *in vitro*, giving scientists a measure of biological damage.

Scientists are also using fertilized chicken eggs to study membrane damage. By carefully stripping off a small portion of the egg shell, they can expose a heavily vascularized membrane on which they can study the effects of various toxins. Even more elaborate tests that measure enzymes and RNA production have been devised.

In vitro testing will not eliminate all animal testing. That's because it does not necessarily replicate the complex functions of an organism or even a body tissue. But scientists may be able to substitute several *in vitro* tests in such instances to get the full picture. Testing for eye irritation, for example, may require data from a battery of tests.

Eugene Ball, professor emeritus at MIT, and chair of Organogenesis, Inc., a biotechnology company in Cambridge, Mass., has developed an artificial skin he calls Living Skin Equivalent (LSE). LSE is a complex cultured skin produced originally for use in skin grafts. But LSE can also be used to test the toxicity of chemicals, providing a fuller picture of the toxic influences. It may also pave the way for the production of other artificial tissues that could be used for toxicity testing.

Despite this and other programs in developing alternatives, there are some significant hurdles yet to overcome. Regulatory agencies, a key link to promoting *in vitro* tests, have done little to develop new standards and acceptable procedures. The EPA, for instance, refuses to accept more humane versions of the eye irritation test, arguing that additional scientific information is needed before the new test can be accepted.

The biggest problem is that federal agencies have not established criteria that alternative tests should meet. This has prevented testing laboratories from using new alternatives. Companies are also reluctant to invest money and time in developing alternative strategies, fearing that they may not be approved, even if they turn out to be effective substitutes. On the bright side, though, the FDA, which started the animal testing to protect citizens, now seems interested in promoting *in vitro* alternatives, thus helping protect animals as well.

Critical Thinking Problems

1. Suppose that studies indicate that eating a bologna sandwich every day and living 20 miles downwind from a chemical plant pose statistically identical health risks to you. The latter risk is likely to provoke some degree of "outrage" in the affected population; the former is not. Why? Can you identify potential "outrage factors"?

2. Are all the factors which enter into risk assessment *rational*? If not, are these any less important than those that are?

3. Most people agree that we have some duties to future generations. If we include these as costs in cost/benefit analysis, how do we quantify them, since we do not know how many generations or people per generation there will be, to whom we are obligated? If you cannot quantify certain "costs," should they be ignored?

4. Is there any absolute hierarchy of human values? Or, when we prioritize our values, is one system just as legitimate as another?

Test Questions

Multiple Choice. Each of the following questions has one correct answer. Circle the letter corresponding to the choice you think best answers the question.

C 1. Acute effects of toxin exposure:

   a. show up 10-20 years after exposure to a chemical.
   b. usually persist for years.
   c. manifest themselves shortly after exposure.
   d. generally result from low-level exposure.

D 2. Cancer:

   a. occurs most commonly in cells that rarely divide.
   b. is always the result of chromosomal changes.
   c. is an acute effect of toxin exposure.
   d. rates increased from 1930 to 1940, but this may have been largely due to better reporting and better diagnosis at death.
   e. a & b
   f. c & d

A 3. The toxicity of a chemical substance:

    a. is strongly influenced by the dose.
    b. is rarely a function of its chemical structure.
    c. is the same no matter if it is inhaled or absorbed through the skin.
    d. is generally greater in older individuals than in young individuals.

F 4. Certain organisms concentrate toxins in fat and other body tissues; this is:

    a. known as biological magnification.
    b. known as biological concentration.
    c. rarely hazardous.
    d. partly responsible for biological magnification.
    e. a & c
    f. b & d

C 5. Chemical substances cause the most profound birth defects if:

    a. given right after fertilization.
    b. given after the organs have formed.
    c. given during organogenesis.
    d. none of the above

C 6. Chronic effects:

    a. show up immediately after exposure to a chemical.
    b. usually are short-lived.
    c. often manifest themselves months or years after exposure.
    d. generally result from high-level exposure.

B 7. Which of the following mutations would be passed on to one's offspring?

    a. a somatic cell mutation
    b. a germ cell mutation
    c. a mutation in the prostate gland
    d. a mutation in the uterine lining

D 8. Toxic substances:

    a. may bind directly to chemicals in cells, upsetting the cell's chemistry.
    b. may alter enzymatic activity.
    c. may cause the release of naturally occurring but harmful chemical substances.
    d. all of the above

Fill in the Blank. For each of the following questions, fill in the blank with the appropriate word or phrase.

1. Cells may break off a tumor and spread throughout the body; the spread of cancer cells is called
_____.

2. A _____ is a structural change in the genetic material of a cell.

3. Agents that cause birth defects are known as _____.

4. Two chemicals may bring about a response that is lower than expected; the chemicals are said to be _____.

5. The _____ is the dose that kills half the animals and is used as a measure of relative toxicity.

6. Cancer cells that break off a tumor set up residence in new locations, forming _____ tumors.

7. The study of the adverse biological effects of harmful substances is _____.

8. The study of birth defects is called _____.

9. A level below which a chemical agent has no effect is called the _____ level.

10. Two or more chemicals may bring about an additive effect in which the response is greater than either alone could elicit. This phenomenon is called _____.

11. The study of hazards in our society is called _____ _____.

12. How much benefit people think they will receive from a given technology is called the _____ benefit.

13. _____ hazards are those created by humans.

14. The _____ risk is the amount of risk a hazard really poses.

15. A _____ analysis is used to weigh the costs and benefits of a given technology.

Answers: 1. metastasis 2. mutation 3. teratogens 4. antagonistic 5. LD50 6. secondary 7. toxicology 8. teratology 9. threshold 10. synergism 11. risk assessment 12. perceived 13. Anthropogenic 14. actual 15. cost-benefit

Short Essay. Write a 250-300 word essay to answer each of the following questions.

1. Explain why so little is known about the effects of toxic substances on human health.

2. Describe the three major provisions of the Toxic Substances Control Act.

3. Describe the process of biological magnification. What causes it and why is it so important to our understanding of toxic substances?

4. Summarize the factors that affect the toxicity of a chemical.

6. Describe the steps you would take to determine if a given risk factor posed an acceptable risk.

7. Sound decision-making requires that we ask three important questions about the effects of our decisions. What are they?

Chapter Supplement. Global Lead Pollution

Fill in the Blank. For each of the following questions, fill in the blank with the appropriate word or phrase.

1. Lead affects many tissues but has an affinity for bone and _____ tissue.

2. Continued high-level exposure to lead may lead to _____, coma, and even death.

3. The single most important source of lead exposure is _____.

4. Lead in drinking water is thought to come primarily from _____ _____ and lead pipes.

5. The most common symptom of individuals exposed to high levels of lead is _____ _____.

6. Numerous reports show that the rate of _____ _____ is higher in couples exposed to high levels of lead in the workplace.

7. Exposure of a woman to lead nearly doubles the risk of her having a _____ child.

8. Adults absorb about 8% - 10% of the lead in their intestines; children absorb about _____.

9. Herbert Needleman found that children with high lead levels in their bodies had significantly lower _____ _____ than those with low lead levels.

10. Studies of lead levels show a strong statistical link between high blood lead levels and _____ blood pressure.

Answers: 1. brain   2. convulsions   3. food   4. lead solder   5. muscular weakness
6. spontaneous abortion   7. retarded   8. 40%   9. IQ scores   10. high

Suggested Readings and Resource Materials

Rescher, Nicholas (1983). *Risk*. Lanham, MD: University Press of America. An interesting and thorough philosophical introduction to the theory of risk evaluation and management.

Sandman, Peter (1986). *Explaining Environmental Risk*. Washington, DC: U.S. Environmental Protection Agency. A fascinating look at "moral outrage factors" and their role in everyday risk assessment.

Videos: For ordering information, see Film/Video Index.

The Council for Chemical Research has produced two videos on toxicology and risk assessment, *Changing Patterns of Cancer in the U.S.* and *Carcinogens, Anticarcinogens, and Risk Assessment*. While these paint a somewhat rosy picture (not surprisingly, considering the sponsorship), they are nonetheless excellent platforms from which to launch discussions and practice critical thinking about controversial issues. Contact The Council for Chemical Research.

Buried in Ice. Presents fascinating evidence that the entire crew of an 1845 sailing expedition died of lead poisoning. A NOVA video. Contact Coronet Film & Video.

Dioxin. A look at the scientific establishment of causal links between toxins and disease. Contact Films for the Humanities & Sciences, Inc.

Toxic Waste: Can We Control It? Focuses on the toxicology of dioxin and PCB's. Contact Richter Productions.

CHAPTER 15

AIR POLLUTION:
PROTECTING A GLOBAL COMMONS

Outline

I. AIR: THE ENDANGERED GLOBAL COMMONS
   A. The Trees Are Responsible
   B. Air Pollutants and Their Sources
   C. Primary and Secondary Pollutants
   D. Toxic Air Pollutants

II. THE EFFECTS OF CLIMATE AND TOPOGRAPHY ON AIR POLLUTION
   A. Brown-Air and Gray-Air Cities
   B. Factors Affecting Air Pollution Levels
      1. Wind and Rain
      2. Mountains and Hills
      3. Temperature Inversions

III. EFFECTS OF AIR POLLUTION
   A. Health Effects
      1. Acute Health Effects
      2. Chronic Health Effects
      3. High-Risk Populations
   B. Effects on Other Organisms
   C. Effects on Materials
   D. Global Warming/Global Change
      1. Global Energy Balance
      2. Upsetting the Balance: The Greenhouse Effect

IV. AIR POLLUTION CONTROL
   A. Cleaner Air Through Better Laws
   B. Cleaner Air Through Technology
      1. Stationary Sources
      2. Mobile Sources
      3. New Ways to Burn Coal
   C. Cleaner Air Through Conservation: A Framework for Personal Actions
   D. Cost of Air Pollution Control

V. CHAPTER SUPPLEMENT. STRATOSPHERIC OZONE DEPLETION
   A. Activities That May Deplete the Ozone Layer
      1. Freons
      2. High-Altitude Jets and Nuclear Explosions
      3. Other Sources of Destruction
   B. Extent and Effect of Depletion
   C. Preventing Ozone Depletion

VI. CHAPTER SUPPLEMENT. ACID DEPOSITION: ENDING THE NIGHTMARE
   A. What Is Acid Deposition?
      1. Wet Deposition
      2. Dry Deposition
   B. Where Do Acids Come From?
   C. The Transport of Acid Precursors
   D. Impacts of Acid Precipitation
      1. Acidification of Lakes
      2. Parks and Wilderness Areas
      3. Effects on Aquatic Ecosystems
      4. Some Human Consequences
      5. New Acid Rain Threat
   E. Solving a Growing Problem
      1. U.S. Drags Its Feet
      2. Prospects for the Future

VII. CHAPTER SUPPLEMENT. INDOOR AIR POLLUTION
   A. Products of Combustion
   B. Formaldehyde
   C. Radioactive Pollutants
   D. Chloroform and Trichloroethylene
   E. Controlling Indoor Air Pollutants

Objectives

After studying this chapter, the student should be able to:

1. List and discuss the impacts of several *anthropogenic* and several *natural* sources of air pollution.
2. Understand the effects of *climate* and *topography* on air pollution.
3. Cite the most common *acute* and *chronic* effects of air pollution.
4. Discuss the various aspects of *global warming*, including causes, effects, predictions, uncertainties, and possible solutions.
5. Characterize the *Clean Air Act* and its major amendments.
6. Propose *legal, technological*, and *behavioral* approaches to air pollution control.
7. List the major activities which deplete *ozone* and discuss the extent, effects, and prevention of ozone depletion.
8. Understand the sources and transport of *acid deposition* precursors and their transformation into acid compounds.
9. Cite the major impacts of increasing ecosystem *acidification*.
10. Summarize the U.S. Government's approach to acid deposition control.
11. Identify the major types and sources of *indoor air pollution*.

Lecture Notes

I. AIR: THE ENDANGERED GLOBAL COMMONS

   A. The Trees Are Responsible
      • Though much air pollution is *natural* in origin, *anthropogenic pollution* poses the biggest environmental threat.

B. Air Pollutants and Their Sources
- *Combustion* is the single largest cause of air pollution today.
- *Incomplete combustion* and the presence of *mineral contaminants* in fuels generate a variety of harmful pollutants.

C. Primary and Secondary Pollutants
- Reactions between atmospheric *primary pollutants* produces a variety of *secondary pollutants.*

D. Toxic Air Pollutants
- Hundreds of *toxic pollutants* are released into the air; the U.S. has not regulated these in the past.

II. THE EFFECTS OF CLIMATE AND TOPOGRAPHY ON AIR POLLUTION

A. Brown-Air and Gray-Air Cities
- *Gray-air* cities are usually characterized by *cold, moist* climates; the major pollutants are *sulfur oxides* and *particulates.*
- *Brown-air* cities are typically in *warm, dry, sunny* climates; the major pollutants are *carbon monoxide, hydrocarbons,* and *nitrogen oxides*; these cities are subject to enshrouding by *photochemical smog.*

B. Factors Affecting Air Pollution Levels
1. Wind and Rain
   - These agents can clear the air but may result in *cross-media contamination.*
2. Mountains and Hills
   - These geographic features can *trap* pollutants in an area, inhibiting dispersion.
3. Temperature Inversions
   - These are *inverted temperature profiles*, either due to movement of large air masses or uneven daily cooling of air and ground, which *trap* pollutants and allow them to *accumulate* over an area.

III. EFFECTS OF AIR POLLUTION

A. Health Effects
1. Acute Health Effects
   - *Acute effects* of air pollution are those experienced *immediately* after exposure.
2. Chronic Health Effects
   - *Chronic Effects* on human health result from *long-term exposure* to air pollution and include several serious *diseases* such as emphysema, bronchitis, and lung cancer.
3. High-Risk Populations
   - Some groups, such as the very *young*, the very *old*, and the *infirm*, are especially susceptible to air pollution's effects.

B. Effects on Other Organisms
- *Livestock, wildlife,* and wild and cultivated *plants* can all be adversely affected by air pollution.

C. Effects on Materials
- Air pollution causes severe damage to *buildings*, most *materials*, and many priceless works of *art.*

D. Global Warming/Global Change
- This is a hot *topic of debate* today.
1. Global Energy Balance
   - Ordinarily, the earth's *energy input* is offset by its *energy output*; thus, a *balance* is maintained.
2. Upsetting the Balance: The Greenhouse Effect
   - Various natural and anthropogenic gases trap heat in our atmosphere; the accumulation of these *greenhouse gases* (CO_2, methane, nitrous oxides, and CFC's) is thought to pose a threat of *global warming*.
   - Effects of increasing levels of greenhouse gases might include *increasing temperature, shifting ocean currents* and *climate zones, altered rainfall patterns, increasing intensity* and *duration* of *storms*, and *rising sea levels*.
   - Should predicted rates of global warming take place, there will be severe *economic, agricultural, sociological, political,* and *ecological repercussions*.
   - The major contributors to global warming are *burning* of *fossil fuels, livestock* and *agriculture*, and *deforestation*.
   - Avoiding global warming can be accomplished through *conservation*, use of *non-contributing energy sources, elimination of CFC's,* and *reforestation*.

IV. AIR POLLUTION CONTROL

A. Cleaner Air Through Better Laws
- The *Clean Air Act* with its amendments is the major legal instrument for air quality protection in the U.S.
- The CAA's provisions aim to *protect* air that is already clean and promote *improvement* in areas already polluted; enforcement is the responsibility of the EPA.
- New revisions of the CAA will address *acid precipitation, toxics,* and the already-addressed *smog* problem.

B. Cleaner Air Through Technology
1. Stationary Sources
   - Reductions in air pollution from *stationary sources* are usually achieved by the removal of pollutants from emissions gases.
   - *Filters, cyclones, precipitators,* and *scrubbers* remove particulates and most polluting gases but generate large amounts of hazardous waste.
2. Mobile Sources
   - Emissions from vehicles are generally controlled by *conversion* to non-polluting substances.
3. New Ways to Burn Coal
   - New combustion techniques such as *magnetohydrodynamics* and *fluidized bed combustion* increase efficiency and reduce air pollution from coal burning.

C. Cleaner Air Through Conservation: A Framework for Personal Actions
- Individuals, corporations, and government can reduce air pollution through *energy conservation*.

D. Cost of Air Pollution Control
- Though costly, numerous studies estimate the *benefits* of air pollution control measures to exceed their *costs*.

V. CHAPTER SUPPLEMENT. STRATOSPHERIC OZONE DEPLETION
*   The *ozone layer* in the stratosphere protects life on earth from harmful levels of *ultraviolet radiation*.

A. Activities That May Deplete the Ozone Layer
1. Freons
    *   *Freons,* or *CFC's*, used as spray propellants, blowing agents, and coolants break down ozone at an alarming rate.
2. High-Altitude Jets and Nuclear Explosions
    *   *High speed, high altitude air-* and *space-craft* emit nitric oxides, which destroy ozone.
    *   *Atmospheric nuclear detonations* have a similar effect.
3. Other Sources of Destruction
    *   *Nitrogen fertilizer* and a variety of chemical *pollutants* can catalyze the breakdown of stratospheric ozone.

B. Extent and Effect of Depletion
*   New techniques for gathering data, sampling the atmosphere, and making projections show that significant ozone destruction, producing *"holes,"* has already taken place.
*   Declines in overall global ozone have been detected and will continue unless immediate action is taken.
*   *Ozone depletion* will disrupt *photosynthesis*, cause an increase in *skin cancer, mutations,* and *cataracts,* and *suppress immunity.*

C. Preventing Ozone Depletion
*   International efforts to stop ozone depletion have centered on the 1987 *Montreal Protocol,* a treaty to guarantee a 50% reduction in CFC and halon production by 1990.

VI. CHAPTER SUPPLEMENT. ACID DEPOSITION: ENDING THE NIGHTMARE

A. What Is Acid Deposition?
*   *Acid deposition* is the deposition of mostly sulfuric and nitric acids from the sky on soils and in bodies of water.
1. Wet Deposition
    *   *Rain, snow, fog,* or *clouds* may deposit acid in wet form.
2. Dry Deposition
    *   *Sulfur* and *nitrogen oxides* may settle directly out of the air or may form *particulates* which, on surfaces, combine with water to form acids.

B. Where Do Acids Come From?
*   *Sources* for acid precursors are *natural* and *anthropogenic.*
*   *Anthropogenic sources* include fossil-fuel fired *power-plants, motor vehicles,* and *ore smelters.*

C. The Transport of Acid Precursors
*   Acid precursors generated in industrial regions may travel hundreds or thousands of kilometers *downwind.*

D. Impacts of Acid Precipitation
1. Acidification of Lakes
    *   Thousands of *lakes* and *streams* in the eastern U.S., Canada, and Scandinavia are alarmingly *acidified*; fish and other aquatic organisms are severely impacted.

2. Parks and Wilderness Areas
   - Several major *parks/wilderness areas* in the U.S. and Canada are suffering the effects of acid deposition.
3. Effects on Aquatic Ecosystems
   - Acidification has *direct* and *indirect effects* on *aquatic ecosystems*; it can mobilize toxic trace elements to which many aquatic species are sensitive.
   - *Melting spring snow* can pose an extra threat to sensitive aquatic species.
   - Effects on aquatic ecosystems have ramifications in adjoining ecosystems connected by their food webs.
4. Some Human Consequences
   - *Forests, crops, lakes* and *streams*, and *human artifacts* are increasingly succumbing to the effects of acid deposition.
5. New Acid Rain Threat
   - *Nitrogen pollution* from acid precipitation is a major cause of excess nutrient enrichment in the Chesapeake Bay.

E. Solving a Growing Problem
   1. U.S. Drags Its Feet
      - The Clean Air Acts' proposed 1990 revision mandates sharp reductions of acid rain precursors; after decades of inaction, this may be too little, too late.
      - Some advocate a *symptom-oriented approach* of neutralizing acid deposition after-the-fact. Besides its cost, this approach is impractical and largely ineffective.
   2. Prospects for the Future
      - Without immediate action, *irreversible* and *widespread damage* may occur; the U.S. is *not* preparing to take immediate action to avert this.

VII. CHAPTER SUPPLEMENT. INDOOR AIR POLLUTION

A. Products of Combustion
   - *Tobacco products*, *gas appliances*, and *stoves* are major sources of combustive indoor air pollution.

B. Formaldehyde
   - *Formaldehyde* is ubiquitous in building and consumer products; it is a known *carcinogen* and *mutagen*.

C. Radioactive Pollutants
   - *Radon gas* is a naturally-occurring radioactive indoor pollutant; it is thought to pose serious risks of lung cancer to the residents of millions of homes in the U.S.

D. Chloroform and Trichloroethylene
   - These *volatile toxins* are often present in drinking water and are given off to the air during hot showers, dishwashing, and laundry washing.

E. Controlling Indoor Pollutants
   - As a recently recognized problem, there is not currently any U.S. federal legislation which directly addresses this problem.

Case Studies

New Process to Reduce Nitrogen Oxides from Smokestacks

Numerous technologies exist to remove sulfur oxides from the smokestacks of factories and power plants. The options for removing nitrogen oxides, however, are limited and expensive -- that is, until recently. Researchers at Argonne (Illinois) National Laboratory have devised a method that will remove more than 70% of the nitrogen oxides from the smokestacks of coal-fired power plants, without affecting the efficiency of the conventional sulfur oxide scrubbers, which can remove more than 90% of this troublesome gas. Researchers added a chemical called ferrous EDTA to the scrubber solution. Nitrogen oxides in the gas bind to the ferrous EDTA. The EDTA then transfers the nitric oxide to the sulfite which is formed when sulfur dioxide in the stack gases enters the scrubber solution.

Ferrous EDTA dramatically increases the trapping rate of nitric oxide. Although it is too early to tell, preliminary estimates suggest that this new technique could cost one tenth to one half as much as the currently available technologies. If put in place, it could dramatically reduce nitrogen oxide emissions, helping reduce photochemical smog and acid deposition, two problems plaguing many parts of the country.

Noise Pollution

Noise is rapidly becoming one of the most widespread environmental pollutants. Few of us can escape it; even when we are enjoying a backcountry camping trip, the silence is broken by the roar of jets, chain saws, and off-road vehicles. Especially noisy are the cities and factories where many of us live and work. To understand noise pollution and its effects, let us first take a look at sound.

Sound is transmitted through the air as a series of waves. For a simple example, take the bass speaker element of a loudspeaker. When the music is loud, the speaker can be seen to vibrate, and a hand placed in front of it can feel the air move. If we could slow down the speaker cone to observe what was happening, we'd see that as it moves outward, it compresses the air molecules in front of it. As the speaker cone returns inward, the air it just compressed expands in both directions, much as a coiled spring would expand when released. This expansion compresses neighboring air molecules slightly farther away. These have the same effect that the outward-pushing speaker cone had. Thus, waves of expansion and compression are set up, transmitting the sound. Air molecules do not travel with the sound, but only oscillate back and forth in the direction the sound is traveling. Sound is a train of high-pressure regions following one another through the air at about 340 meters per second (760 miles per hour).

Sound can be described in terms of its loudness and its pitch, or frequency. Loudness is measured in *decibels* (dB). The decibel scale encompasses a wide range of volume. The lowest sound the human ear can detect is set at 0 dB; this is the threshold of hearing. In the decibel scale a tenfold increase in sound intensity is represented by a 10 dB increase on the scale. That is, a 10 dB sound is 10 times louder than a 0 dB sound; a 20 dB sound is 10 times louder than a 10 dB sound and 100 times louder than a 0 dB sound.

Pitch, or frequency, is a measure of how high or how low a sound is. Bass notes played by a tuba have a low pitch, and a violin's treble notes have a high pitch. Pitch is measured in cycles (that is, waves) per second. This is the number of compression waves passing a given point each second. The higher the pitch, the larger the number of cycles per second. Cycles per second are commonly called hertz (Hz), after the German physicist Heinrich Rudolf Hertz.

The human ear is sensitive to sounds in the range of 20 to 20,000 hertz. Sounds below 20 hertz are not detected by the human ear and are described as *infrasonic*. Sounds above the audible range are called *ultrasonic*.

Ambrose Bierce wrote that "noise is a stench in the ear, and the chief product of civilization." To the scientist, noise is any unwanted, unpleasant sound. Beyond that, it is hard to say with any certainty what a group of people would consider noise. The rumble of construction machinery at a building site might be pleasing to the owner of the new building but insufferable to the doctor whose office is next door.

What any individual considers noise depends on his or her background, mood, occupation, location, and hearing ability. But the time of day, the duration and volume of a sound, and other factors also contribute to our judgment. A sound may be pleasant when it is soft but noisy when it is loud, or it may be acceptable when you generate it but obnoxious when someone else does. People generally agree that the louder a sound is, the more annoying it becomes and the more likely people are to describe it as noise.

Sources of noise fall into four categories: transportation, industrial, household, and military. As the world becomes more dependent on technology, noise pollution will grow worse. Of greatest concern are noises from off-road vehicles, construction, air traffic, home appliances, and surface transportation. Noise affects us in many ways. It damages hearing, disrupts our sleep, and is an annoyance in our everyday lives. It interferes with conversation, concentration, relaxation, and leisure.

Our hearing declines with aging and exposure to noise. Natural hearing loss results from degeneration of the hair cells, sensory cells in the ear that translate sound into nerve impulses. This natural decline is presumably brought about by infections in the inner ear and natural aging of the sound receptors.

Men generally suffer a greater loss of hearing with age than women. This difference probably results from factors other than sex, such as firing guns or exposure to noise at work. Therefore, what appears to be a natural decline may in fact be brought about by factors under our own control.

Many sounds from a variety of sources impinge upon our ears. Some of these, if loud and persistent enough, can cause premature degeneration of the hair cells. Experts believe that 1 in every 10 to 20 people suffers some hearing loss from anthropogenic noise. We have all been exposed to noise so loud that we experienced a momentary decrease in our ability to hear. This is called a *temporary threshold shift*. A loud concert, a party with a loud stereo and lots of noisy friends, a drive in the car with the windows open, noisy machinery, or gunfire can all deafen us for a little while.

A permanent loss of hearing, or a *permanent threshold shift*, occurs after continued exposure to loud noise. Recent studies suggest that continuous, long-term exposure to noise levels as low as 55 dB can permanently damage hearing. Noise of this level is common in many factories and jobs, especially in construction and mining. Even city traffic noise can damage the hearing of people exposed on a regular basis. It should be no surprise, then, that a 20-year-old New York City resident hears as well as a 70-year-old tribesman from Africa's grasslands.

As a general rule, the higher the sound level, the less time it takes to induce a permanent threshold shift. In addition, intermittent noise is generally less hazardous than continuous noise. Different frequencies, for example, do less damage than the higher-pitched sounds at the same loudness. Explosions (130 dB) and other extremely loud noises can cause instantaneous damage to the hair cells, resulting in deafness. Noise levels over 150 dB can severely damage the hair cells, rupture the eardrum, and displace the tiny bones in the ear, the *ossicles*, which convey sound waves from the eardrum to the hair cells.

According to many sources, occupational noise is slowly deafening millions of Americans. Large numbers of Americans work at jobs where the noise levels are over 80 dB. Military personnel are victims of noise from tanks, jets, helicopters, artillery, and rifles. Studies show that about half of the soldiers who complete combat training suffer so much hearing loss that they no longer meet the enlistment requirements for combat units. Bars, nightclubs, discotheques, and traffic noise (especially diesel trucks and buses) are other important contributors to the deafening of America.

The importance of good hearing cannot be emphasized enough. In children it is important for learning language. The loss of hearing impairs our ability to understand what's being said. Communication with family, friends, and co-workers can be severely impaired, causing increased tension not only because the sufferer can't understand what's being said but also because deafened individuals may talk annoyingly loud.

Because speech comprehension is so crucial, techniques have been devised to measure social impairment caused by hearing loss. The *social adequacy index* takes into account effects of hearing loss in pitch and loudness. Studies show that there can be a fairly large intensity loss without loss of social adequacy. However, a loss of frequencies -- for example, the inability to hear sounds of 4000 hertz -- greatly impairs social functioning. A classic study compared social adequacy in weavers, who had been exposed to a 100 dB work environment, with that in a control group of people not exposed to loud noises. Nearly three-fourths of the weavers said they had difficulties at public meetings, compared with 5% of the control group. Eighty percent of the weavers experienced difficulty talking to strangers, compared with 16% of the controls. Sixty-four percent of the weavers had difficulty understanding phone conversations, compared with 5% of the controls.

Noise affects sleep in many ways: (1) it may prevent us from falling asleep as soon as desired, (2) it may keep us from sleeping at all, (3) it may wake us during the night, and (4) it may alter the quality of sleep, leaving us irritable.

When jet aircraft travel faster than the speed of sound, they create a sonic boom. A sonic boom is a cone-shaped wave that trails behind the jet. Residents in the flight paths of supersonic military jets and the supersonic transports operated by France, England, and the Soviet Union complain about interrupted sleep, rest, conversation, and radio and television reception caused by sonic booms. Studies in the United States and England show that most people are startled by sonic booms, even if they live in an area where they are common. Because there is no warning of its coming, the sonic boom invariably catches people off guard. Sonic booms do minor damage to buildings, monuments, and other structures in a state of poor repair. Very little is known about their effects on animals. Sonic booms are likely to become more frequent occurrences as the world's military capability expands and as population centers grow. Careful siting of military bases and regulation of population growth around bases and in flightpaths could help reduce exposure to sonic booms. Commercial supersonic transport jets designed to carry passengers and cargo have not been successful in this age of declining fossil fuel supplies, so our major exposure will continue to be from military aircraft.

Noise pollution has received little attention compared with other forms of air pollution. One reason is that hearing loss is generally progressive: victims are unaware of the gradual loss in auditory acuity. Workers who are exposed to loud noises eventually become accustomed to them, partly because their hearing declines.

126

Noise control can be carried out on many different levels. Changing the design of machinery and other products can cut turbulence and vibration. Better urban planning can isolate people from noisy railroads, highways, factories, and airports. Legal controls on noise emissions can also be helpful. Many countries, including Japan, Norway, the Netherlands, Sweden, Switzerland, the United Kingdom, Denmark, France, Italy, and Canada, have regulations to control noise from motorized vehicles. In the United States, the *Noise Control Act* (1972) authorized the EPA to establish maximum permissible noise levels for motor vehicles and other sources. Individual cities and towns have passed noise ordinances.

Noise in US workplaces is controlled by the Occupational Safety and Health Administration. The workplace standard is 90 dB for an eight-hour exposure, a level many authorities believe is too high. The agency can issue abatement orders for noise violations. They require the employer to first tackle the problem through engineering and design changes in the equipment. Should these prove infeasible, ear guards must be worn by workers, or workers must be removed regularly from noisy jobs to quieter jobs to reduce their overall exposure. Personal protective equipment is a less desirable solution, because it is uncomfortable to wear and also blocks out important sounds or signals necessary for worker safety.

In May 1977, the EPA released its first comprehensive national plan for reducing noise and preventing hearing loss. It called for a reduction of the average daily exposure to no more than 65 dB in the short term and 55 dB in the long term, product labeling, cooperation from states and local agencies, federal policies to encourage noise buffer zones around transportation facilities, and the use of quieter equipment on federal construction projects. To date, however, noise control has been pushed to the back burner in favor of seemingly more pressing environmental problems like hazardous wastes.

Critical Thinking Problems

1. During the Reagan Administration and to some extent during President Bush's tenure, the government policy has been to continue to study major air pollution problems like acid rain and global warming in order to avoid "overreacting" and spending unnecessarily on controls. What, in your opinion, is the most dangerous aspect of this wait-and-see policy?

2. Some nations actually stand to *benefit* from predicted climate changes due to global warming. If so, how can we expect them to cooperate in international efforts to address the problem?

3. Many U.S. residents identify deforestation in Third World countries as a major contributor to global warming and call for measures to reduce or stop tropical deforestation. Are they being hypocritical, in that the U.S. reached its current state of development by doing the very things its citizens are now asking less-developed countries not to do?

4. In what sense can liming acidified lakes be likened to straightening deck chairs on the Titanic? Is breeding acid-resistant trout analogous to breeding a gas-resistant canary for use in mines?

Test Questions

Multiple Choice. Each of the following questions has one correct answer. Circle the letter corresponding to the choice you think best answers the question.

C   1.   The air we breathe is a mixture of gases; the major component is:

        a. oxygen.
        b. carbon dioxide.
        c. nitrogen.
        d. argon.

D   2.   Of the six major air pollutants, which is the most harmful to plants?

        a. particulates
        b. hydrocarbons
        c. carbon monoxide
        d. sulfur oxides

B   3.   Brown air cities:

        a. are older industrial cities.
        b. are characterized by high levels of nitrogen oxides and carbon monoxide.
        c. are found in colder, humid climates.
        d. are characterized by older industries such as steel.

A   4.   Emphysema:

        a. is a chronic, incurable disease of the lungs.
        b. is characterized by irritation of the bronchi and persistent coughing.
        c. is linked to smoking but not to urban air pollution.
        d. none of the above

C   5.   Which of the following pollutants takes a heavy toll on buildings and statues?

        a. carbon monoxide
        b. nitrogen dioxide
        c. sulfur dioxide
        d. hydrocarbons

A   6.   Which of the following is a major source of carbon monoxide?

        a. transportation
        b. industry
        c. solid waste disposal
        d. power plants

D   7.   The incomplete combustion of organic compounds results in the formation of:

        a. carbon monoxide.
        b. hydrocarbons.
        c. sulfur dioxide.
        d. a & b
        e. b & c

B   8.   Gray air cities:

        a. are younger cities like Denver and Los Angeles.
        b. are characterized by high levels of particulates and sulfur oxides.
        c. are found in drier, hot climates.
        d. none of the above

D   9.   Radiation inversions:

        a. usually occur over very large areas.
        b. result when a mass of high-pressure air settles over a region.
        c. form early in the morning.
        d. start forming a few hours before sunset as soon as the air near the ground begins to cool.

C   10. The greenhouse effect:

        a. results from an accumulation of carbon monoxide.
        b. may result in a rapid melting of the polar ice caps.
        c. could raise the sea level 200 to 300 feet but probably over many centuries.
        d. none of the above

Fill in the Blank. For each of the following questions, fill in the blank with the appropriate word or phrase.

1.   Heat is also known as _____ radiation.

2.   _____ standards were set for air pollutants in order to protect human health.

3.   The _____ _____ policy allows industry expansion in nonattainment areas by allowing a new company to pay an existing company to cut back its emissions.

4.   Particulates are removed by _____ precipitators.

5.   Finely powdered coal is mixed with sand and limestone and then fed into a boiler in _____ _____ combustion.

6.   Pollutants released directly into the environment from anthropogenic sources are called _____ pollutants.

7.   New cars are equipped with _____ _____, devices that reduce CO and hydrocarbon emissions by completing combustion.

8. Large particulates may be removed from air streams by passing the waste gases through _____, metal cylinders that cause the air to swirl and force the particulates to strike the walls and fall to the bottom where they can be removed.

9. _____ air pollution standards were set to protect plants, visibility, and materials.

10. _____ is a chronic inflammation of the bronchial tubes brought on by cigarette smoking and air pollution.

11. _____ cancer is the most prevalent form of cancer in the United States.

Answers: 1. infrared   2. Primary   3. emissions offset   4. electrostatic   5. fluidized bed
6. primary   7. catalytic converters   8. cyclones   9. Secondary   10. Bronchitis   11. Lung

Short Essay. Write a 250-300 word essay to answer each of the following questions.

1. Why is anthropogenic air pollution generally more harmful than natural pollution?

2. Describe the two ways temperature inversions can form.

3. Describe some of the chronic and acute health effects of air pollution.

4. How are nitrogen oxides formed during combustion and why are they so difficult to control?

5. What is photochemical smog and how is it formed?

6. What environmental factors affect air pollution levels in a given region?

Chapter Supplement. Stratospheric Ozone Depletion

Fill in the Blank. For each of the following questions, fill in the blank with the appropriate word or phrase.

1. The ozone layer is located in the outer layer of the _____.

2. The ozone layer screens out harmful _____ light.

3. Spray can propellants and refrigerants, or _____ (several answers possible), can destroy the ozone layer.

4. The breakdown of spray can propellants and refrigerants is stimulated by sunlight; this breakdown is called _____.

5. High-altitude jets produce _____ _____, which can damage the ozone layer.

Answers: 1. stratosphere   2. ultraviolet   3. freons, fluorocarbons or chlorofluoromethanes
4. photodissociation   5. nitric oxides

Chapter Supplement. Acid Deposition: Ending the Nightmare

Multiple Choice. Each of the following questions has one correct answer. Circle the letter corresponding to the choice you think best answers the question.

D   1.   Which of the following is true regarding acid precipitation?

        a.   The two major acids in acid precipitation are sulfuric and hydrochloric acid.
        b.   Acid precipitation is rain and snowfall with a pH greater than 7.
        c.   Natural sources of acidity are the most important ones.
        d.   It has been growing in intensity and range for over 3 decades in the United States and Europe.

B   2.   Sulfuric acid:

        a.   is emitted mostly from coal-fired power plants.
        b.   forms in the atmosphere from sulfur dioxide gas and water.
        c.   is the more difficult of the two acids in acid rain to control.
        d.   none of the above

A   3.   Acidification of lakes:

        a.   occurs most readily in areas of acid rainfall and shallow soils.
        b.   is not yet a problem in the United States.
        c.   does very little to the aquatic life until the pH reaches 3.
        d.   is the primary cause of fish kills during the spring snow melt.

C   4.   Neutralizing lakes:

        a.   is an inexpensive way to prevent acidification.
        b.   results in long-term recovery with only one application of lime.
        c.   is a short-term solution that has limited value.
        d.   a + c

D   5.   Acid precipitation:

        a.   in some cases may fertilize crops and accelerate their growth.
        b.   may damage crops by changing the soil chemistry.
        c.   may damage buds and impair future growth.
        d.   all of the above
        e.   none of the above

Chapter Supplement. Indoor Air Pollution

Fill in the Blank. For each of the following questions, fill in the blank with the appropriate word or phrase.

1.   Pollutants produced in our homes and offices are called _____ _____ pollutants.

2.   Cigarettes, gas furnaces and gas stoves all produce _____ _____, a colorless, odorless air pollutant that can impair oxygen transport in the blood.

3. _____ is a pollutant given off by plywood, wood paneling, and furniture.

4. The radioactive gas _____ is produced from radium in rocks and soil.

5. Sulfur and _____ oxides are lung irritants produced by some indoor combustion sources, such as kerosene heaters.

Answers: 1. indoor air   2. carbon monoxide   3. Formaldehyde   4. radon   5. nitrogen

Chapter Supplement. Noise Pollution

Fill in the Blank. For each of the following questions, fill in the blank with the appropriate word or phrase.

1. Loudness is measured on a _____ scale.

2. Sounds below the range of hearing are called _____.

3. Loss of hearing with age is called _____.

4. A temporary loss of hearing from a loud noise is called a temporary _____ shift.

5. The bones of the ear which convey sound from the eardrum to the organ of Corti are called _____.

Answers: 1. decibel   2. infrasound   3. presbycusis   4. threshold   5. ossicles

Suggested Readings and Resource Materials

Committee on Global Change, et. al (1989). *Ozone Depletion, Greenhouse Gases,* and *Climate Change.* New York: National Academy Press. Results of a symposium attended by representatives of major institutions in the field of atmospheric sciences.

Flavin, Christopher. *Slowing Global Warming: A Worldwide Strategy.* Washington, DC: WorldWatch Institute.

Graedel, T. and P. Crutzen, "The Changing Atmosphere" in *Scientific American*, September, 1989, pp. 58-69. Excellent overview.

Lyman, Francesca et al. (1990). *The Greenhouse Trap: What We're Doing to the Atmosphere and How We Can Slow Global Warming.* Beacon Press. Full of advice for addressing this threat.

Postel, Sandra. *Air Pollution, Acid Rain, and the Future of Forests.* Washington, DC: WorldWatch Institute.

Schneider, Stephen (1989). *Global Warming: Are We Entering the Greenhouse Century?* San Francisco: Sierra Club Books. The new, thorough treatment of this growing controversy.

Wellburn, Alan (1988). *Air Pollution and Acid Rain.* New York: Wiley and Sons. Focuses on how pollution operates on living systems as a whole.

Videos: For ordering information, see Film/Video Index.

Air Pollution: Outdoor; Air Pollution: Indoor; Radon; and *Acid Rain* are some of the films on air pollution distributed by Films for the Humanities & Sciences.

Acid Rain: New Bad News. Contact WGBH Boston.

Acid Rain: Requiem or Recovery? Contact National Film Board of Canada.

Cooperation Across Boundaries: The Acid Rain Dilemma. A look at the international political effects of acid rain. Contact Bullfrog Films.

Hole in the Sky. A NOVA investigation of the Antarctic ozone hole. Contact Coronet Film & Video.

Hot Enough for You? NOVA looks at the greenhouse effect. Contact Coronet Film & Video.

CHAPTER 16

WATER POLLUTION:
PROTECTING ANOTHER GLOBAL COMMONS

Outline

I.   WATER AND WATER POLLUTION
    A. Point and Nonpoint Sources
    B. Some Features of Surface Waters

II. TYPES OF WATER POLLUTION
    A. Nutrient Pollution and Eutrophication
        1. Organic Nutrients
        2. Inorganic Plant Nutrients
        3. Eutrophication and Natural Succession
    B. Infectious Agents
    C. Toxic Organic Water Pollutants
    D. Toxic Inorganic Water Pollutants
        1. Mercury
        2. Nitrates and Nitrites
        3. Salts
        4. Chlorine
    E. Sediment
    F. Thermal Pollution

III. GROUNDWATER POLLUTION

IV. OCEAN POLLUTION
    A. Oil in the Seas
    B. Plastic Pollution
    C. Medical Wastes and Sewage Sludge

V.   WATER POLLUTION CONTROL
    A. Legal Controls
    B. Control Technologies
        1. Primary Treatment
        2. Secondary Treatment
        3. Tertiary Treatment
    C. Personal Solutions

Objectives

After studying this chapter, the student should be able to:

1.   Identify the major *types, sources*, and *effects* of water pollution.
2.   Define *point* and *nonpoint source pollution* and give several examples of each.

3. Discuss *natural* and *cultural eutrophication* and *succession*.
4. Characterize *groundwater* with regard to its susceptibility to pollution and resistance to recovery.
5. List the major types and sources of pollution in the *oceans* and discuss the effects of each.
6. Outline a plan for water pollution control which effectively integrates legal, technological, and personal solutions.

Lecture Notes

I. WATER AND WATER POLLUTION
   - *Water pollution* is any physical or chemical change in water which adversely affects organisms.

   A. Point and Nonpoint Sources
      - *Point sources* are discrete, easily identified and controlled locations of concentrated pollution discharge.
      - *Nonpoint sources* are large, less discrete areas over which dispersed pollutants are generated and discharged.

   B. Some Features of Surface Waters
      - *Standing systems* are still, freshwater ecosystems such as lakes and ponds; their stagnant nature makes them particularly *susceptible* to pollution.
      - *Flowing systems* are running, freshwater ecosystems such as rivers and streams; their rapid water replacement enables them to *purge* pollutants fairly quickly.

II. TYPES OF WATER POLLUTION

   A. Nutrient Pollution and Eutrophication
      - *Nutrients* in excessive amounts become *pollutants*.
      1. Organic Nutrients
         - These include *feedlot* and *slaughterhouse wastes, sewage treatment effluent,* and some *industrial wastes.*
         - Organic nutrients are *oxygen demanding substances* since their metabolism by bacteria is aerobic.
         - The greater the organic nutrient load of water, the greater the *biochemical oxygen demand.*
      2. Inorganic Plant Nutrients
         - These nutrients, primarily *nitrogen* and *phosphorus*, stimulate the growth of aquatic plants; this can result in *excess aquatic plant growth* and *oxygen depletion.*
         - *Nitrogen fertilizer* and phosphate-containing *laundry detergents* are major sources of inorganic plant nutrient pollution in freshwater systems.
      3. Eutrophication and Natural Succession
         - *Eutrophication* is nutrient enrichment of a body of water; it can be either *natural* or *cultural.*
         - *Eutrophication* and *erosion* result in the *natural succession* of lakes and ponds into swamps and, finally, dry land; humans have greatly accelerated this process.

   B. Infectious Agents
      - *Pathogenic organisms* may enter water through *sewage effluent, animal wastes* and *processing byproducts*, and certain *wildlife species.*

135

C. Toxic Organic Water Pollutants
  • Thousands of these may contaminate water and pose *aesthetic, environmental*, or *human health* problems.

D. Toxic Inorganic Water Pollutants
  1. Mercury
     • A *common, toxic heavy metal*, mercury is widespread and harms aquatic organisms and humans.
  2. Nitrates and Nitrites
     • These come from *fertilizer* and *animal* and *human wastes*; in high concentrations, they can poison infants who drink contaminated water.
  3. Salts
     • *Salts*, often used on roads during winter, can kill nearby organisms and pollute ground and surface water.
  4. Chlorine
     • A widely used disinfectant, *chlorine* can react with organic compounds to produce various carcinogens and mutagens in water.

E. Sediment
  • The most *voluminous* water pollutant in the U.S., *sediment* is generated by *forestry, agriculture, mining*, and *construction*.
  • *Sedimentation* aggravates pollution problems, fills in lakes and streams, and damages human property.

F. Thermal Pollution
  • Unnatural changes in water temperature which adversely affect organisms are instances of *thermal pollution*.
  • Thermal pollution *increases metabolism* and *decreases dissolved oxygen* in aquatic systems and may interfere with *reproduction* and *migration* of some species.
  • *Power plants* are the major sources of thermal pollution.
  • A sudden, dramatic change in water temperature is *thermal shock*; this can be fatal for many organisms.

III. GROUNDWATER POLLUTION
  • *Groundwater* is subject to contamination from a variety of surface sites and activities.
  • Common pollutants include *chlorides, nitrates, heavy metals, hydrocarbons, pesticides*, and *organic solvents*; many are known carcinogens.
  • Since groundwater renewal and recovery is quite slow, *prevention* is the best method of protection.

IV. OCEAN POLLUTION

A. Oil in the Seas
  • Sources include *natural seepage, well blowouts, tanker* and *pipeline discharges, tanker spills* and *urban runoff*.
  • The effects of oil pollution vary with the *amount* and *rate* of release, *location*, and *water temperature*.

B. Plastic Pollution
  • Discarded *plastics* ensnare, entangle, starve, or suffocate hundreds of thousands of fish, marine mammals, and birds yearly.

C. Medical Wastes and Sewage Sludge
- Illegal dumping of *medical wastes* and legal and illegal dumping of *sewage* and *sewage sludge* have caused environmental damage and pose a serious human health threat.
- *Legislation* aimed at stemming these practices has been enacted.

V. WATER POLLUTION CONTROL

A. Legal Controls
- The *Clean Water Act* primarily regulates point source pollution.
- Though enhanced *sewage treatment* can effectively reduce point source pollution, these gains are often offset by increasing nonpoint source pollution.
- *Zoning ordinances, soil conservation programs* and other *legal requirements* can help reduce nonpoint source pollution and protect groundwater supplies.

B. Control Technologies
1. Primary Treatment
   - *Primary sewage treatment* consists of mechanical screening and settling and removes large objects and solids.
2. Secondary Treatment
   - *Secondary sewage treatment* utilizes microorganisms to digest biodegradable organic matter.
3. Tertiary Treatment
   - Specialized filters and processes can remove chemicals left by secondary treatment; however, such *tertiary sewage treatment* is costly.
   - Use of *holding ponds, land disposal*, and other innovative techniques can further reduce pollution from sewage treatment systems.

C. Personal Solutions
- Each of us can take steps to minimize our *personal contribution* to water pollution problems and to minimize our overall environmental impact.

Case Study

Road Salt: Calculating the Real Costs

The Canadian Supreme Court ruled recently that the Province of Ontario must compensate two farmers whose apple and peach orchards were damaged by salt that had been applied to nearby highways. The court agreed that fruit trees that were more than 100 meters away from the road had been poisoned by the salt.

Twenty-five-dollar-per-ton road salt is also America's weapon of choice for de-icing some 2.5 million kilometers (1.5 million miles) of roadway in snowy cities. Although salt may seem like a bargain, the effects of its use suggest otherwise. Road salt erodes auto bodies, eats into pavement, corrodes bridges, pollutes groundwater, and kills nearby trees. Increasingly, salt from roadways is polluting groundwater in eastern and northern cities, forcing authorities to close both private and public wells in New England and several upper midwestern states. In Massachusetts, over 100 private and municipal wells have been closed as a result of salt contamination.

Since salt causes so many problems, one might wonder why we aren't using safer alternatives. Several options exist. One of them is a corn-starch based substitute and the other is calcium-magnesium acetate. Local authorities in the U.S. and Canada, however, argue that these alternatives are too costly and haven't been tested adequately for safety. These alternatives may cost 10 to 25 times more than salt. Larry Hudson, a senior project manager at the New York State Energy Research and Development Authority in Albany, however, found that when the economic and environmental impacts of traditional road salt were factored into the cost, the practice was far more expensive than potentially safer methods. The real cost of road salt, he estimates, is about $1600 a ton. That includes the cost of additional road and bridge maintenance, economic loss to consumers as a result of car rust, damage to underground pipelines and electrical cables, groundwater contamination, and the destruction of aquatic and roadside vegetation.

According to biologists, the effects of road salt are visible wherever it collects in highway drainages. In mountainous areas where road runoff drains into a single wetland, the effects of salt can be profound. The normal salinity of fresh water is roughly 250 parts per million, but after a winter of road salting the concentration in the runoff can range from 10,000 parts per million to 25,000 parts per million. Although the salt is diluted when it is mixed with fresh water, it still causes problems for fish eggs and fry.

Although no city has yet managed to ban salt, Madison, Wisconsin decided in 1975 to use a salt-sand mixture only on major roads, and sand alone on its side streets. The city today uses 42% less salt than it did 10 years ago. Similar efforts taken in Canada and the United States could greatly reduce the damage while officials look for alternatives.

Critical Thinking Problems

1. It's tempting to blame drunk tanker captains, governmental inertia, and corporate greed for the plastics problem and water pollution disasters like the Exxon *Valdez* oil spill. But, don't we all share responsibility for these problems? Identify the ways in which *your* lifestyle, job, and consumer preferences have increased the likelihood of such disasters and problems.

Test Questions

Multiple Choice. Each of the following questions has one correct answer. Circle the letter corresponding to the choice you think best answers the question.

C   1.   Nonpoint water pollution sources:

    a. are generally easy to control.
    b. include sewage treatment plants.
    c. produce about half of the United States' surface water pollution.
    d. a & b
    e. b & c

A   2.   The shallow waters along the shore of a stream constitute the:

    a. littoral zone.
    b. hypolimnion.
    c. lotic zone.
    d. limnetic zone.

B   3.   Organic pollutants:

    a. retard bacterial growth.
    b. indirectly cause oxygen levels in streams and rivers to fall.
    c. stimulate algal growth.
    d. come mostly from synthetic fertilizers used to fertilize crops.

E   4.   Eutrophication:

    a. is the accumulation of sediment in lakes.
    b. is accelerated by inorganic water pollutants.
    c. occurs most readily in shallow lakes.
    d. a & b
    e. b & c

C   5.   Primary treatment of sewage:

    a. is relatively expensive but effective in removing toxic chemicals in sewage.
    b. removes most of the nitrates and phosphates in sewage.
    c. primarily removes solids and organic materials.
    d. none of the above

D   6.   Land disposal of sewage:

    a. can be used to recharge groundwater.
    b. helps enrich soils and prevent water pollution.
    c. may create some problems because of harmful bacteria that can be incorporated in plants and consumed by humans and other animals.
    d. all of the above

B   7.   Secondary treatment of sewage:

    a. is rarely practiced because of its expense.
    b. relies on bacteria and other organisms to eliminate much of the organic matter in sewage.
    c. primarily removes solid wastes.
    d. removes toxic wastes and radioactive materials.

E   8.   Thermal pollution:

a. may interfere with normal fish migration and spawning.
b. has little influence on the life cycle of aquatic organisms.
c. can be put to good use by using the heat to promote the growth of commercially important fish and shellfish.
d. a & b
e. a & c
f. b & c

C   9.   Mercury:

a. is most harmful in its inorganic form.
b. is converted into the inorganic form by bacteria.
c. is a powerful neurotoxin.
d. is not biologically magnified.

B   10.   Cultural eutrophication:

a. is the deposition of sediments from erosion in lakes.
b. results from the release of inorganic plant nutrients from feedlots and other sources.
c. is the accelerated conversion of a lake into dry land.
d. none of the above

Fill in the Blank. For each of the following questions, fill in the blank with the appropriate word or phrase.

1.   Sharp changes in temperature cause _____ _____, causing the sudden death of fish.

2.   The deposition of sediment on streambeds is called streambed _____.

3.   _____ is a highly reactive chemical used to disinfect drinking water.

4.   Deep lakes that lack plant nutrients are said to be _____.

5.   The standard measurement for oxygen depletion in streams is the _____ _____ _____.

6.   _____ combine with the hemoglobin in red blood corpuscles, reducing their ability to carry oxygen.

7.   An excessive growth of algae caused by pollution is called an algal _____.

8.   The open water of a lake which is penetrated by sunlight is called the _____ zone.

9.   About _____ of the oil in the ocean comes from natural seepage from offshore deposits.

Answers: 1. thermal shock 2. aggradation 3. Chlorine 4. oligotrophic 5. biochemical oxygen demand 6. Nitrites 7. bloom 8. limnetic 9. one-half

Short Essay. Write a 250-300 word essay to answer each of the following questions.

1. What are the major sources of sediment in water, and how can they be controlled?

2. What are the major sources of groundwater pollution? How can groundwater pollution be reduced or eliminated?

3. Describe the series of events that occur after organic pollutants, such as sewage, enter a stream. Be certain to discuss pollutant levels, bacterial populations, fish populations, oxygen levels, and recovery.

4. Define the term nonpoint water pollution source. Give some examples. Why is it generally easier to control point sources of water pollution than nonpoint sources?

5. Describe the sources and effects of plastics in the ocean.

Suggested Readings and Resource Materials

Maurits la Rivière, J.W., "Threats to the World's Water" in *Scientific American*, September, 1989, pp. 80-107. Thorough treatment of a complex issue.

Sierra Club Legal Defense Fund (1989). *The Poisoned Well*. Washington, DC: Island Press. Outlines new strategies for groundwater protection.

Videos: For ordering information, see Film/Video Index.

Are You Swimming in a Sewer? A NOVA video which examines outdated ideas and new evidence concerning the oceans' ability to assimilate wastes. Contact Coronet Film & Video.

Changing Tides Along the Mediterranean. Examines problems stemming from modern industrial society's impact on a delicate ocean system and their possible solutions. Contact The Video Project.

Pointless Pollution: America's Water Crisis. A look at nonpoint source pollution across the U.S. Narrated by Walter Cronkite. Contact Bullfrog Films.

The Great Lakes: Troubled Waters. Examines pollution on the Great Lakes today. Contact Umbrella Films.

Upstream - Downstream: New Orleans and River Contamination. Contact Cine Research Associates.

Your Water, Your Life. Examines how water cycles through the environment and becomes polluted, and shows how the public is responding to the growing threat of groundwater contamination. Contact University of Minnesota.

CHAPTER 17

PESTICIDES:
A DOUBLE-EDGED SWORD

Outline

I. A HISTORICAL OVERVIEW
    A. Development of Chemical Pesticides
    B. Exploration, Exploitation, and Reflection
        1. Exploration
        2. Exploitation
        3. Reflection

II. INTEGRATED PEST MANAGEMENT
    A. Education and Monitoring
    B. Environmental Controls
        1. Increasing Crop Diversity
        2. Altering the Time of Planting
        3. Altering Plant and Soil Nutrients
        4. Controlling Adjacent Crops and Weeds
        5. Introducing Predators, Parasites, and Disease Organisms
    C. Genetic Controls
        1. Sterile Male Technique
        2. Developing Resistant Crops and Animals
    D. Chemical Controls
        1. Second-Generation Pesticides
        2. Pheromones
        3. Insect Hormones
        4. Natural Chemical Pesticides
    E. Cultural Controls

III. ECONOMICS, RISK, AND PEST CONTROL

IV. HERBICIDES IN PEACE AND WAR
    A. Peacetime Uses: Pros and Cons
    B. Controversy Over Wartime Use of 2,4-D and 2,4,5-T
        1. Ecological Effects of Agent Orange
        2. Health Effects of Agent Orange

V. UNFINISHED BUSINESS

Objectives

After studying this chapter, the student should be able to:

1. Outline the *historical development* of modern chemical pesticides through its three phases.

2. List and describe the benefits, techniques, and limitations of *integrated pest management*.
3. Identify the factors which must be included in a thorough *cost/benefit analysis* of any pest control program.
4. List and describe the pros and cons of *herbicide* use.
5. Discuss the use of *Agent Orange* in the Vietnam War, including the ethical problems it has raised.

Lecture Notes

I. A HISTORICAL OVERVIEW

    A. Development of Chemical Pesticides
- *Pesticides* are pest-killing chemicals.
- *First-generation* pesticides were simple but mostly either *toxic* or *ineffective*.
- *Second-generation* pesticides began with DDT; these are synthetic organic compounds, of which thousands have been developed.
- *Pesticides* fall into *three chemical families: chlorinated hydrocarbons, organic phosphates*, and *carbamates*.

    B. Exploration, Exploitation, and Reflection
      1. Exploration
- The first of three developmental stages in pesticide use was *exploration*; during this phase, the various uses and potential benefits of pesticides were discovered.
      2. Exploitation
- During the *exploitation* phase, pesticide use was greatly expanded with little information or concern about adverse environmental effects.
- *Problems* encountered during this phase include *destruction of beneficial insects, development of pest genetic resistance, and health effects in nontarget organisms and humans*, especially chemical and farm workers, rural residents, and consumers.
      3. Reflection
- Due to the unanticipated adverse impacts generated during the phase of exploitation, a period of caution or *reflection* followed; the beginning was marked by Rachel Carson's *Silent Spring*.

II. INTEGRATED PEST MANAGEMENT
- This system calls for the integrated use of *environmental, genetic, chemical*, and *cultural* pest control; with properly educated farmers and increased pest monitoring, results can be impressive.

    A. Education and Monitoring
- Education of the grower and frequent pest *monitoring* are necessary prerequisites to successful IPM.

    B. Environmental Controls
- These *alter* the *environment* to disfavor the pests.
      1. Increasing Crop Diversity
- *Heteroculture* and *crop rotation* help prevent rapid growth of pest populations.
      2. Altering the Time of Planting
- This technique can thwart pests by removing their food supply.
      3. Altering Plant and Soil Nutrients
- By *manipulating nutrient levels* in soils and thus plants, some pests can be suppressed.

4. Controlling Adjacent Crops and Weeds
   - This can help control pests by either *eliminating food* or *habitat* for them or by *luring* them off more valuable crops.
5. Introducing Predators, Parasites, and Disease Organisms
   - Use of these techniques mimics or supplements natural *biotic environmental resistance factors* which regulate pest populations.

C. Genetic Control
1. Sterile Male Technique
   - This involves releasing *sterilized males* of the pest species, which mate with wild females who thus do not produce offspring.
2. Developing Resistant Crops and Animals
   - *Genetic engineering* and *artificial selection* can lead to the development of pest-resistant crops and livestock.

D. Chemical Controls
1. Second-Generation Pesticides
   - With sparing, timely, and appropriate application of low-toxicity, specific, and non-persistent pesticides, many of the benefits of these chemicals can be retained without accompanying ecological and human health damage.
2. Pheromones
   - *Pheromones* are chemicals, such as sex attractants, released externally by organisms; though *expensive*, they can effectively control some pests by *luring* them to traps or *interfering* with their breeding success.
3. Insect Hormones
   - Insect life cycles can be interrupted through the timely use of *juvenile* and *molting hormones*.
4. Natural Chemical Pesticides
   - Various *plant extracts* have insecticidal or repellant properties.

E. Cultural Controls
   - These various techniques offer alternatives to harsh chemical pesticides and are often quite effective.

III. ECONOMICS, RISK, AND PEST CONTROL
   - A thorough and fair cost/benefit analysis would prove many pest control efforts too costly to continue.
   - Since many "benefits" of pesticide use are cosmetic or otherwise trivial, consumers can help by lowering their aesthetic expectations at the produce counter.

IV. HERBICIDES IN PEACE AND WAR

A. Peacetime Uses: Pros and Cons
   - *Benefits* and *drawbacks* of *herbicide* use are numerous; serious concerns focus on their tendency to discourage good husbandry in farmers and their possible threats to water and human health.

B. Controversy Over Wartime Use of 2,4-D and 2,4,5-T
   - The most commonly used herbicide during the war in *Vietnam* was *Agent Orange*: a 50-50 mixture of 2,4-D and 2,4,5-T.

1. Ecological Effects of Agent Orange
   - *Destruction* and *damage* to ecosystems from the use of this herbicide is *extensive*; even today, the hardest-hit areas show little sign of recovery.
2. Health Effects of Agent Orange
   - *Birth defects, miscarriages*, cancers and various *physiological* and *psychological disorders* have been linked to the herbicides used and to *dioxin*, a contaminant of 2,4,5-T.
   - Some studies which attempt to link health effects in Vietnamese, Vietnam veterans, and their offspring to herbicide exposure have proved inconclusive; nevertheless, many are convinced that the link is real.

V.   UNFINISHED BUSINESS
   - The *Federal Insecticide, Fungicide, and Rodenticide Act* (FIFRA) and the *Federal Food, Drug, and Cosmetic Act* regulate pesticides in the U.S.
   - Though valuable for their registration requirements and set tolerance levels, these laws are *difficult to enforce* and easily circumvented, and are grossly *inadequate* in certain respects.

Case Studies

MPTP Pollution and Parkinson's Disease

In 1983 Dr. J.W. Langston made a bizarre discovery. Several young men and women were admitted to his hospital in a catatonic-like stupor. Completely immobile, the patients were unable to feed themselves, to move their limbs, or to talk. Several months of intensive detective work showed that the hopelessly "frozen" patients were drug addicts who had happened on a laboratory-synthesized heroin, one of the many new "designer drugs." This particular batch had been improperly made in the basement of the supplier's home and was contaminated with a chemical substance called MPTP, a pyridine compound.

Researchers have since discovered that MPTP attacks the substantia nigra, a portion of the midbrain involved in muscle movement. The substantia nigra is the region that gradually deteriorates in victims of the debilitating malady known as Parkinson's disease, which usually develops late in life. Parkinson's victims suffer from tremors and partial or complete paralysis. Individuals exposed to MPTP, even tiny amounts, develop symptoms of Parkinson's disease within a few days of exposure. Some scientists believe MPTP accelerates the naturally occurring nerve cell degeneration in the substantia nigra.

What is disturbing about this discovery is that MPTP is strikingly similar to a number of common industrial chemicals and widely used pesticides. It most closely resembles the herbicide paraquat. This has led some researchers to believe that Parkinson's disease may actually be caused by environmental pollution from industry and from agricultural pesticides.

Opponents of this view argue that, at the cellular level, Parkinson's disease is not that similar to paraquat toxicity. A number of studies have failed to show a link between industrialization and Parkinson's disease. Other studies have shown no increase in the disease in the United States since the 1940s, at which time pollution levels began climbing. Thus, at a 1985 meeting held at the National Institutes of Health, researchers largely agreed that the disease is not produced by environmental contamination.

No sooner had these researchers left their meeting than André Barbeau and his colleagues at the Research Institute of Montreal announced the startling results of a study on the incidence of Parkinson's disease in Quebec province. The researchers showed, quite to the surprise of the academic community, a remarkable correlation between the use of pesticides and the incidence of the disease. The statistical correlation was so high as to be irrefutable. The researchers stressed, however, that herbicides are just one of many neurotoxins capable of destroying the nerve cells of the substantia nigra and causing this disease. They noted that a large number of industrial pyridines were also suspect.

Further evidence supporting an environmental cause of Parkinson's disease, according to Barbeau and his colleagues, is that the malady was nonexistent before the Industrial Revolution. The incidence of the disease increased sharply through the 1800s and reached a plateau in the early decades of the 1900s, for unknown reasons. However, Barbeau warns that the rising use of paraquat and other chemically similar substances could cause a rise in Parkinson's disease in years to come.

Clearly, the jury is still out. At this time, Barbeau's work stands pretty much alone in showing a link between MPTP and Parkinson's disease. Further research is needed to determine if the link does indeed exist and what we can do about it.

Source: Adapted from Lewin, R. (1985). "Parkinson's Disease: An Environmental Cause?" *Science* (July 19):257-258.

Controlling the Coyote

Some species exhibit a resistance to human control that boggles the mind. Take the coyote, for example. A predator and scavenger with an inherent fear of humankind, this small relative of the dog flourishes today in an ever-widening range. Where wolves once howled, the coyote now roams, feeding on insects, rodents, small birds, carrion of all sorts, and, yes, an occasional sheep or house cat that wanders too far from the safety of its home.

The coyote is an animal revered by some for its cunning and resistance to human extirpation. It is the environmentalist's cause célèbre. But to others, like the angry sheepherders of the West, the animal the Navajos dubbed "God's Dog" is a loathsome creature unfit to live. Controlling the coyote, one of the few large predators left in the United States, has become a national obsession of sorts.

The heart of the controversy is this: Ranchers maintain that coyotes kill thousands of sheep annually, costing the industry $100 million a year. Environmentalists, on the other hand, assert that this estimate is grossly exaggerated. They put the damage at about one-tenth of that, and they argue that the environmental and economic costs of control, which exceed $18 million annually, far exceed benefits. They say, further, that we can control coyote damage at a fraction of the current cost.

Coyote populations have been "controlled" by a variety of techniques: shooting, aerial hunting, poisoning, spring-activated guns loaded with cyanide, trapping, guard dogs, and denning-burning or gassing coyotes in their dens. One of the most popular weapons before 1972 was a poison called Compound 1080, or simply 1080. Compound 1080 (sodium monofluoroacetate) is a "supertoxin." A single teaspoon of 1080 is so toxic it could kill 100 average people. A healthy adult who handles meat laced with this deadly compound, without gloves or precautions, risks getting sick. A child who handles poisoned meat can die by licking her or his fingers.

For many years, ranchers and government predator-control agents laced meat and animal carcasses with 1080 and dropped it from airplanes in an attempt to eradicate coyotes. Environmentalists protested: Although the poison was intended primarily for coyotes that preyed on sheep, they said, many nontarget species such as badgers, eagles, dogs, foxes, and raccoons also fed on bait and died. Such indiscriminate poisoning, environmentalists argued, was unwise.

In 1972, under heavy pressure from the environmental community, President Richard Nixon banned the use of 1080 for predator control on federal lands and in federally sponsored programs. That same year the EPA banned the chemical for commercial sale, effectively putting a stop to its use on private property as well. What convinced the EPA to remove the chemical from a long list of chemical poisons was 1080's likely role in 13 human fatalities and 6 nonfatal poisonings. The chemical, they said, was just too dangerous to humans to be used.

In February 1982, under intense pressure from the powerful livestock industry, President Ronald Reagan rescinded Nixon's ban. This left it up to the EPA to determine if 1080 could once again be used. Despite vigorous protests from the environmental community, the EPA reauthorized the use of 1080, but only in sheep collars. Sheep collars contain small packets of 1080 in a liquid form and are worn around the sheep's neck, where the coyote typically strikes. When a coyote bites into the collar, it receives a lethal dose of 1080. Currently, 1080 is registered for use in Wyoming, South Dakota, New Mexico, Texas, and Missouri, but not more than 250 collars are in use and then under extraordinarily tight restrictions.

Supporters of 1080 collars argue that this control measure is far more selective than other baiting techniques. It should eliminate only the troublesome coyotes, they say, and save a lot of animals that would be killed if 1080 were used more traditionally. But environmentalists argue these points: First, they say, scavengers such as ravens, vultures, and small mammals will feed on coyotes poisoned with 1080 as well as the tainted meat of sheep killed by coyotes. Consequently, nontarget species will continue to die. Second, unscrupulous ranchers could extract 1080 from the collars and use it in dangerous ways. Third, other less costly and less risky options are available.

For example, in many western states, where sheep are big business, ranchers leave their flocks unattended throughout much of the grazing season. Here, the introduction of guard dogs could greatly cut down on coyote predation. Guard dogs have been used successfully in Europe for hundreds of years. Living with the flock, they protect sheep from marauding coyotes. The Hampshire College Farm Center in Amherst, Massachusetts, for example, has placed hundreds of its dogs in 31 states since 1978. The dogs' protective instincts are so strong that they need virtually no training. Pups are simply placed in a sheep herd early on and left with them. Exposed to sheep so early in life, scientists say, the dogs begin to consider themselves part of the flock and are quick to bound after any approaching coyote.

Guard dogs are one of the most economical and effective ways to control coyotes. A 1984 survey showed that 36% of the farms experiencing heavy predation reported no attacks after guard dogs were brought in. And because a dog can be leased for $50 a year, saving one ewe per year pays for the dog several times over. However, many ranchers do not trust dogs or are unwilling to try a new idea. And some are so used to poison and other control methods that they look skeptically on this time-tested but forgotten solution. As a result, they continue to press for a relaxation of controls on 1080.

Guard dogs are not the only ecologically sound way to control sheep-killing coyotes. Other measures include the use of coyote-proof fences, noisemakers, and taste aversion. Taste aversion is still in the experimental phase but could prove to be effective. Ranchers inject a dead ewe or lamb with lithium chloride, a compound that produces nausea in any animal that feeds on the meat.

Coyote control has frustrated American ranchers for decades because coyotes exhibit a great deal of resiliency. Following a heavy coyote "harvest," for example, females increase their litter size in the next season. The average litter of three pups can jump to seven to nine that year, thus negating control efforts.

What is needed, argue some biologists, is a way for coyotes, sheep, and humans to live peacefully side by side. That doesn't mean wiping out all coyotes with poisons or putting an end to the economically important sheep industry, but rather a change in traditional management--most notably, a shift to more ecologically sound techniques, among them our faithful friend, the dog.

Critical Thinking Problems

1. In 1962, Rachel Carson was branded a heretic by many in the agricultural community and in government. Over time, of course, she has been largely exonerated. Jeremy Rifkin, the self-appointed watchdog of genetic engineering and biotechnology, is today labelled a heretic by those same groups. Are the critics right this time, or will Rifkin be exonerated too? What are some possibly unforeseen or ignored effects of biotechnology which could confirm Rifkin's fears?

2. Many environmentalists urge a return to organic farming. Is this practical? Can we feed the world's population without using pesticides? If not, are we *obligated* to use pesticides to maintain production?

Test Questions

Multiple choice. Each of the following questions has one correct answer. Circle the letter corresponding to the choice you think best answers the question.

B 1. Chlorinated hydrocarbons:

   a. are first-generation pesticides.
   b. are noteworthy because of their persistence in the environment.
   c. break down fairly rapidly and therefore pose little risk.
   d. rarely are biomagnified in the food chain.

D 2. DDT:

   a. is a first-generation pesticide.
   b. was developed in the 1970s to combat malaria.
   c. is a carbamate.
   d. causes egg-shell thinning in flesh-eating birds.

B 3. Genetic resistance to pesticides:

   a. is not a problem because only a small percentage of an insect population is resistant.
   b. leads farmers to use higher doses.
   c. is found only in insect populations.
   d. can be combatted in the long term by developing new chemical pesticides.

C   4.   Increasing crop diversity:

    a. aids very little in controlling insects and other pests.
    b. can be brought about by infusing new genes into domestic crops.
    c. can be brought about by intercropping and crop rotation.
    d. increases the amount of food available to pests and results in widespread crop damage.

A   5.   The sterile male technique:

    a. works in many cases because many female insects breed only once during their lifetime.
    b. relies on the use of pheromones, chemicals that attract fertile males away from reproductively capable females.
    c. was successful in controlling the medfly in California.
    d. all of the above

Fill in the Blank. For each of the following questions, fill in the blank with the appropriate word or phrase.

1.   _____ _____ pesticides were simple preparations made of ashes, sulfur, arsenic compounds, and so on.

2.   Today, about _____ of the annual crop production is lost to pests.

3.   _____ was awarded the Nobel Prize for his discovery of DDT.

4.   The _____ are widely used pesticides that are less persistent than all other chemical forms.

5.   An _____ is proliferation of insects once held under control by predatory insects.

6.   Because of growing pesticide resistance, cotton fields in Central America once sprayed 8 times per year are now sprayed _____ to _____ times.

7.   The buildup of a pesticide in the food chain is called _____ _____.

8.   At least _____ U.S. farm and chemical workers are seriously poisoned each year by pesticides.

9.   Rachel Carson's book _____ _____ pointed out many of the impacts of pesticide use.

10.   A pesticide that kills a wide variety of insects is called a _____ _____ biocide.

11.   Planting two or more crops side by side in a given field is called _____.

12.   The herbicides 2,4-D and 2,4,5-T function similar to plant growth-stimulating hormones known as _____.

13.   Agent Orange, used during the Vietnam war, was contaminated with a chemical called _____, which is believed to be responsible for many of the side effects of the use of this defoliant.

14.   Natural plant repellants, _____, may prove useful in our attempts to create genetically resistant crops.

15. _____ control methods are designed to alter the biotic and abiotic environment, making it inhospitable to pests.

Answers: 1. First-generation   2. two-fifths   3. Muller   4. carbamates   5. upset   6. 30, 40
7. biological magnification   8. 100,000   9. *Silent Spring*   10. broad-spectrum   11. heteroculture
12. auxins   13. dioxin   14. allomones   15. Environmental

Short Essay. Write a 250-300 word essay to answer each of the following questions.

1. Pesticide use and development has gone through three stages--exploration, exploitation, and reflection. Describe each one.

2. Define the term integrated pest management. List the major techniques of integrated pest management.

3. List and describe the pros and cons of herbicide use.

Suggested Readings and Resource Materials

League of Women Voters. *America's Growing Dilemma: Pesticides in Food and Water.* Washington, DC: League of Women Voters. A new citizen's action guide to public policy on the issues of pesticide residues and alternative agriculture practices.

Mott, Lawrie and K. Snyder (1987). *Pesticide Alert: A Guide to Pesticides in Fruits and Vegetables.* San Francisco: Sierra Club Books. A timely, comprehensive guide to pesticides in the foods we buy and eat.

Postel, Sandra. *Defusing the Toxics Threat: Controlling Pesticides and Industrial Waste.* Washington, DC: WorldWatch Institute.

Videos: For ordering information, see Film/Video Index.

Herbicide Trials. Tells the story of a group of Nova Scotian citizens who went to court to prevent herbicide spraying in their area. Contact Umbrella Films.

Putting Aside Pesticides. Concerns long-term effects of indiscriminate pesticide use and examines some alternative pest-control strategies. Contact Films for the Humanities & Sciences, Inc.

CHAPTER 18

HAZARDOUS WASTES: PROGRESS AND POLLUTION

Outline

I. HAZARDOUS WASTES: COMING TO TERMS WITH THE PROBLEM
   A. Love Canal: The Awakening
   B. The Dimensions of a Toxic Nightmare
   C. Lust--It's Not What You Think

II. ATTACKING HAZARDOUS WASTES ON TWO FRONTS
   A. What to Do With Today's Waste
      1. The Legal Approach
      2. Technological Answers
      3. Disposing of High-Level Radioactive Wastes
      4. Disposing of Low- and Medium-Level Radioactive Wastes
      5. Some Obstacles
   B. Cleaning Up Past Mistakes

III. CHAPTER SUPPLEMENT. SOLID WASTES: SOLVING A GROWING PROBLEM
   A. The Input Approach
   B. The Throughput Approach
      1. Reuse
      2. Recycling
      3. Obstacles to Recycling
      4. Recycling on the Rise
      5. Procuring Recycled Materials
   C. The Output Approach
      1. Dumps and Landfills
      2. Ocean Dumping
      3. Composting
      4. Incineration

Objectives

After studying this chapter, the student should be able to:

1. Discuss the national significance, implications, and effects of the *Love Canal* toxic waste nightmare.
2. Define *LUST* and suggest remedial actions which might effectively deal with this problem.
3. Outline a plan for dealing with hazardous wastes which integrates *legal, technological*, and *behavioral* solutions.
4. Define *input, throughput*, and *output* with regard to solid waste management.
5. Debate the pros and cons of *landfills* versus *incineration* for solid waste disposal.
6. List the advantages of *reuse* over *recycling*, and of *recycling* over *disposal* of solid wastes.

151

7. Address the major *obstacles* currently preventing final solutions to our nuclear, toxic, and solid waste disposal problems.

Lecture Notes

I. HAZARDOUS WASTES: COMING TO TERMS WITH THE PROBLEM

  A. Love Canal: The Awakening
   • *Hazardous wastes* are byproducts of industry that pose a *threat* to the *environment*.
   • *Love Canal* is a tragic public health and environmental disaster; it symbolizes our past disregard for the basic rule that "there is no away."
   • As a result of negligent (though legal) dumping of toxic wastes at Love Canal, the *health* and *investments* of nearly a thousand families were damaged or destroyed and millions of dollars will be spent for *compensation* and *cleanup*.

  B. The Dimensions of a Toxic Nightmare
   • The huge *amount* of waste produced and past irresponsible *disposal* practices combine to create a toxic waste nightmare.
   • In the past, toxic wastes were disposed of largely by use of two criteria: *cost* and *convenience*; effects of this negligence include *groundwater* and *soil contamination*, human and other animal *disease* and *death, costly* cleanup attempts and remediation efforts, and forced *abandonment* of homes and small towns.

  C. LUST--It's Not What You Think
   • *Leaking underground storage tanks*, "LUST," pose serious threats to groundwater worldwide.
   • *Costs* of LUST correction may be prohibitively high.

II. ATTACKING HAZARDOUS WASTES ON TWO FRONTS

  A. What to Do With Today's Waste
   1. The Legal Approach
    • The *Resource Conservation and Recovery Act* (RCRA) is legislation aimed at improving waste-disposal practices in the U.S.
    • Though well-intentioned, RCRA has its *drawbacks*, including enforcement difficulties and stimulation of illegal dumping.
   2. Technological Answers
    • Changes in *manufacturing, monitoring, recycling*, and *disposal* technologies can cut waste substantially.
    • New technologies include *detoxification, incineration, low-temp decomposition*, and *perpetual storage*.
   3. Disposing of High-Level Radioactive Wastes
    • Currently, the U.S. has no disposal facility for *high-level radioactive wastes* generated by weapons manufacture and nuclear energy production.
    • By law, the Federal government must choose a waste disposal site, build and license a repository there, and begin accepting high-level wastes within a decade; public opposition, though, may delay this.
   4. Disposing of Low- and Medium-Level Radioactive Wastes
    • *Low-level radioactive wastes* are currently landfilled in *Nevada, Washington*, and *South Carolina*.

- There is no repository yet for *medium-level radioactive waste*, though DOE has built a *Waste Isolation Pilot Plant* in New Mexico which might be licensed to receive these wastes.
  5. Some Obstacles
     - Overall, while total amounts of toxic waste generated in the past few years have decreased, *disposal problems* have intensified.
     - The move away from land- and water-based disposal practices has created a new hazard, *toxic waste incineration*.

B. Cleaning Up Past Mistakes
   - *"Superfund"* legislation established *liability* for wastes from cradle to grave, and established a *fund* for site cleanup and property damage compensation.
   - Administrative problems, cost, and mismanagement have made the Superfund cleanup program largely *ineffective*; better solutions are needed.

III. CHAPTER SUPPLEMENT. SOLID WASTES: SOLVING A GROWING PROBLEM
   - The huge amounts of *solid waste* we generate represent a squandering of energy, resources, and money; it is a result of *population growth*, increasing *consumerism* and *affluence*, and a combination of *marketing, governmental*, and *societal factors* which stimulate consumption and waste generation.
   - The *goals* of modern solid waste management focus on *source reduction* and *minimum-impact disposal*.

A. The Input Approach
   - The *input approach* involves *source reduction*: reducing the amount of materials consumed and thus waste generated.
   - Three input approach techniques are *increasing product lifespan, reducing materials used*, and *reducing consumption*.

B. The Throughput Approach
   - This largely consists of *reusing* and *recycling* materials before they enter the waste stream.
   1. Reuse
      - Many items commonly thrown out as waste can be *reused* one or more times.
      - By reducing waste, reuse lessens all the problems associated with waste disposal.
   2. Recycling
      - *Recycling* a product to make more products *saves energy, resources, money, pollution, jobs*, and *aesthetics*.
   3. Obstacles to Recycling
      - These are few *technological* obstacles to recycling; rather, the barriers are *political, governmental, economic*, and *attitudinal*.
   4. Recycling on the Rise
      - Spiralling *landfill costs, energy* and *resource shortages*, and *pollution problems* will encourage recycling efforts in the U.S.
   5. Procuring Recycled Materials
      - High recycling rates can be achieved only if a strong *market* for recycled products is maintained.

C. The Output Approach
   - This focuses on ways to safely and economically *dispose* of waste.

1. Dumps and Landfills
   - While *sanitary landfills* are environmentally preferable to *open dumps*, they are still *energy-* and *resource-intensive, potentially polluting*, and generally *undesirable* as neighbors.
2. Ocean Dumping
   - This practice raises serious concerns over *ecosystem damage, toxin biomagnification*, and *aesthetic degradation* of oceans and beaches.
3. Composting
   - Though *composting* has its drawbacks, it can be an effective way of dealing with abundant organic matter.
4. Incineration
   - *Waste-to-energy plants*, or *incinerators*, can reduce waste volume and recover energy from wastes, but they emit toxic *air pollution* and generate hazardous *ash* for disposal.

Case Studies

Getting Tough on Polluters

For years, part of corporate America has been dumping hazardous wastes in rusty drums in empty fields, sometimes without even burying them. More resourceful companies have diverted them through hidden pipes to rivers and streams. Others have mixed them with oil that is later used to control road dust or is burned for fuel in apartment and office buildings. Still others have dumped their wastes in sandy-bottomed pits, where they gradually seep into the groundwater. Some waste-disposal companies rented warehouses, stored their wastes, then vanished, leaving the owner with a warehouse full of dangerous chemicals. In one sordid affair, Massachusetts officials found that truckers carrying liquid waste just drove down the turnpike at night and opened their spigots, letting toxic liquids spill out on the highways.

Thanks to tougher state and federal laws, it's getting harder for companies to dump their hazardous wastes. But the days of illegal waste disposal are far from over. According to an EPA estimate, one out of seven American companies that generates hazardous wastes may have disposed of them illegally in the past two years.

All across the nation, citizens are banning together to fight illegal disposal. Their battle is being aided by state and federal officials who, when tipped off about potential violators, are staking out the companies, gathering evidence, and helping prosecutors put many of their officials behind bars. In Los Angeles, for instance, a toxic strike force now operates with investigators from the police, fire, and sanitation departments and from the Los Angeles County Health Department. One of the task force's first targets was David Peairs, who was under contract to dispose of hazardous wastes for several companies. Peairs simply diverted the liquid wastes into the sewer, reaping huge profits in the process. With police cordoning off the plant, strike force members went to work examining company records and inspecting the facilities. Peairs eventually pleaded no contest, was fined $100,000, and was sentenced to three months in jail. This was the first time in the state's history that an individual had gone to jail for violating an environmental law.

In 1984, the Los Angeles strike force gathered evidence that led to the conviction of the president of American Caster. He received a $20,000 fine and a six-month jail sentence for ordering his employees to bury highly flammable toxic wastes away from the company grounds. The strike force and the court are sending a message to white-collar executives who knowingly dump hazardous wastes. The message is that, if caught, they will be fined and could very well end up in jail.

Even the EPA has gotten into the act in recent years. Its agents, trained in fire-arms, stakeouts, and self-defense, are recruited from police departments, the FBI, and the Treasury Department. On the frontier of criminal enforcement, these agents often risk their lives "busting" hazardous waste violators. "Disposing of hazardous wastes is more profitable than selling narcotics," notes one special agent of the EPA's Office of Criminal Enforcement. Because of these profits, violators may resort to violence.

In 1983, EPA investigators helped crack a case against the A.C. Lawrence Leather Company, in New Hampshire. The company had received $1.5 million from the EPA to help construct a project to demonstrate the feasibility of a special waste-treatment system. Instead of building the system, officials of the company pocketed the money and piped the waste into a nearby stream. The EPA got wind of the deceit. After three months of investigation, EPA agents arrested and won a conviction against the president, vice-president, and three members of the board of directors.

EPA agents were deputized in 1984 as federal marshals for the first time, a move that gave them the power to enforce U.S. toxic substance laws. The biggest problem facing the EPA's 32 agents is the large number of violators. Because cases are generally complicated, no agent can handle more than two at a time. With months of investigation and trial time, agents are spread too thin. Even though states and the FBI provide assistance from time to time, the task of enforcing the hazardous waste laws is overwhelming. Compounding the lack of personnel is a severe budgetary constraint.

Critics argue that increased personnel and funding are necessary to put tighter reins on illegal hazardous disposal. Violators must know that they stand a reasonable chance of getting caught and convicted before they will halt the dangerous and illegal waste disposal practices so rampant today.

Source: Adapted from Wexler, M. (1985), "Strike Force," *National Wildlife* 23(4):38-41; and Adler, B. (1985), "Risky Business," *Sierra* 70(6):22, 24, 25, 27.

Dirty Diapers

Americans throw away millions of disposable diapers each year--enough to reach to the moon and back seven times. Each child uses an estimated 6,500 disposable diapers from birth to the glorious day (from a parent's perspective) when he or she is successfully toilet trained. That amounts to 18 million "disposable" diapers each year. Most of the plastic-lined disposable diapers end up in landfills where they sit over many decades, slowly decomposing.

The disposable diaper is a symbol of an economy built on waste. Manufacturers profit through the short lifespan of their products and none better exemplifies the logic than the disposable diaper. Today, 90% of diaper sales are for disposables. Disposable diapers are big business--valued at more than $3 billion a year.

The single-use diaper has an outer layer of water-proof plastic. Sandwiched between the plastic and the inner layer is a layer of cotton-like absorbent material made from wood pulp. To increase the absorbency, manufacturers add a super-absorbent polymer that turns to a gel as it absorbs urine.

Designed for convenience, the diaper has become part of a growing waste stream. Well over 90% of the soiled disposable diapers end up in landfills where experts think they could eventually create a human health hazard. Feces and urine leaching from the landfill can enter groundwater, polluting private and public wells. Although single-use diaper manufacturers recommend rinsing feces in the toilet, most parents don't.

Besides creating a health hazard, disposable diapers are an incredible waste of material. Disposable diapers manufacturers use an estimated 90,000 metric tons of plastic and 720,000 metric tons of wood pulp each year. Nationwide, disposable diapers constitute 2% to 4% of the solid-waste stream. Disposal of the diapers costs American cities and towns an estimated $300 to $350 million a year.

Many people who are concerned with public health, groundwater, landfill space, and the waste of materials have switched to washable cotton diapers, which can be reused 80 to 200 times each. For these people, two options are available: washing the diapers themselves or using a diaper service. Diaper services, which pick up dirty diapers each week and supply parents with clean ones in return, today serve fewer then 2% of American families with children under 3, according to one estimate. But thanks to an increase in environmental consciousness, diaper services, are experiencing considerable growth in their business.

A growing number of parents are finding that the "old way" isn't so difficult, and that improvements in cloth diapers have made them considerably more convenient than most people think. Helping make diapers more convenient are new wraps and Velcro patches that help hold the diaper in place, eliminating the need for safety pins and the stiff plastic pants that make babies hot. Washable diapers are also cheaper than disposable diapers, by as much as 40%. They reduce solid waste and may even reduce the incidence of diaper rash. Cotton diapers require slightly more work on the part of the parents, but it is time well spent protecting our environment.

Critics of disposable diapers are concerned about chemicals in them. Small amounts of dioxin, for example, have been found in paper products, and critics also worry about the gels used to absorb water. The American Academy of Pediatrics and the Consumer Product Safety Commission have stated there is no cause for alarm. The Environmental Protection Agency and the American Paper Institute also argue that dioxin in disposable diapers is not a threat to infants. But these assertions are not based on research. Critics worry that dioxin could be extracted from disposable diapers by creams applied to a baby's skin. Dioxin, they say, might then enter the bloodstream.

Advocates of the disposable diaper raise questions about the risks of cloth diapers from diaper services, pointing out that these companies use bleach, antiseptics, and fabric softeners. Clearly, more work is needed to settle the controversy.

Some proponents of washable diapers believe that governments should provide economic incentives to diaper services. Such subsidies will help reduce landfilling and could create additional jobs. Outright bans on disposable diapers may also be effective.

In 1989, a Colorado company began marketing a nearly 100% biodegradable diaper. Although this reduces one problem--the low rate of decomposition in landfills--it does nothing to reduce municipal solid waste or the waste of raw materials and energy needed to manufacture disposable diapers. What's needed are solutions that solve all of the problems--and the best one, besides limiting family size--is to use washable diapers.

Critical Thinking Problems

1. Since high-level radioactive wastes must be isolated for thousands of years, many future generations will necessarily be saddled with the responsibility of guarding and monitoring wastes from which they will have received no benefit. Is there such a thing as intergenerational justice, and, if so, does our production of nuclear waste violate it?

2. In what sense can the EPA be said to be playing "musical dumps" when it cleans up a toxic waste site? *Is* there any way to actually solve a toxic contamination problem, or is moving it further "away" ultimately the best we can do?

Test Questions

Multiple choice. Each of the following questions has one correct answer. Circle the letter corresponding to the choice you think best answers the question.

C   1.   Which of the following is true regarding hazardous wastes?

    a.   Experts estimate that there are about 1,000 hazardous waste sites in need of clean up.
    b.   Superfund money has been used to clean up hundreds of sites in the United States.
    c.   Americans produce well over a ton of hazardous wastes per person per year.
    d.   a & b
    e.   b & c

D   2.   The EPA Superfund:

    a.   is used to fund research on hazardous wastes.
    b.   was established primarily with tax revenues from the general public.
    c.   is used to compensate victims of hazardous wastes.
    d.   is strictly limited to use for the cleanup of hazardous waste dumps on private and public land.

A   3.   The Nuclear Waste Policy Act:

    a.   established a strict timetable for the Department of Energy to choose future sites for radioactive waste disposal.
    b.   requires the Congress to set up a program for disposing of radioactive waste at sea.
    c.   funds active research on waste disposal.
    d.   all of the above

A   4.   Which of the following is the best way of reducing the hazardous waste problem?

    a.   process manipulation to reduce waste production
    b.   chemical treatment to neutralize wastes
    c.   secured landfills to store wastes permanently
    d.   storage of wastes in secured waste piles

B   5.   Which of the following is not required by the Resource Conservation and Recovery Act?

    a.   establishment of a list of potentially hazardous wastes
    b.   premanufacture notification to the EPA of hazardous substances
    c.   establishment of regulations for handling hazardous wastes
    d.   setting up of permit requirements for hazardous waste disposal

Fill in the Blank. For each of the following questions, fill in the blank with the appropriate word or phrase.

1. _____ landfills are lined by synthetic liners or thick layers of clay to prevent leakage.

2. Radioactive wastes can be bombarded with neutrons to _____ some of the radionuclides into harmless substances.

3. Some toxic wastes can be destroyed by mixing them with air and heating them under high pressure; this process is called _____ decomposition.

4. Redesigning industrial processes to reduce hazardous waste production is called _____ manipulation.

5. Use of wells to dispose of hazardous wastes, called _____ _____ injection, can create many problems.

Answers: 1. Secured 2. transmute 3. thermal 4. process 5. deep well.

Short Essay. Write a 250-300 word essay to answer each of the following questions.

1. In what ways have hazardous wastes been improperly disposed of in the past?

2. Discuss the pros and cons of the incineration of hazardous waste at sea.

3. Discuss the best and the least desirable ways of handling the hazardous waste problem.

Chapter Supplement. Solid Wastes: A Growing Problem

Fill in the Blank. For each of the following questions, fill in the blank with the appropriate word or phrase.

1. Reducing waste by conservation and reducing our dependency on unnecessary packing is an example of a(n) _____ approach.

2. Most solid waste is dumped in _____ landfills and covered daily with dirt to cut down on insect and rodent problems.

3. _____ is a process in which organic wastes are allowed to decay into an organic-rich substance useful as a soil conditioner.

4. _____ is the high-temperature decomposition of organic wastes in anaerobic conditions.

5. _____ can effectively reduce the volume of the municipal waste stream by returning useful materials to manufacturers.

Answers: 1. input 2. sanitary 3. Composting 4. Pyrolysis 5. Recycling

Suggested Readings and Resource Materials

Blumberg, L. and R. Gottlieb (1989). *War On Waste: Can America Win its Battle With Garbage?* Washington, DC: Island Press. Examines the causes of our waste problems and offers practical advice to those faced with finding solutions to this problem.

Newsday (1989). *Rush to Burn: Solving America's Garbage Crisis?* Washington, DC: Island Press. A through critique of incineration as a solution to our solid waste problems.

Pollock, Cynthia. *Mining Urban Wastes.* Washington, DC: WorldWatch Institute.

Videos: For odering information, see Film/Video Index.

Down in the Dumps. A look at hi-tech approaches to solving the solid waste problem. Contact Films for the Humanities & Sciences.

From Sea to Shining Sea. A film which covers Greenpeace's efforts to stop the flow of toxins from a Ciba-Geigy plant into a coastal bay. Brings in government ineffectiveness and civil disobedience. Contact Bullfrog Films.

Hazardous Waste: Who Bears the Cost? A good general introduction and awareness-raiser. Contact Umbrella Films.

The Killing Ground. An ABC News "Close-up," examines the threat of toxic wastes and the problems caused by illegal or unregulated dumping. Excellent film. Contact ABC Wide World of Learning Inc.

The Rush to Burn. Examines incineration, its safety regulation, and alternatives. Contact The Video Project.

The Toxic Gold Rush. A look at disposal facilities for toxic wastes and their drawbacks and problems. Contact Films for the Humanities & Sciences, Inc.

Waste Not: Reducing Hazardous Waste. Industrial Case Studies. Contact Bullfrog Films.

CHAPTER 19

ENVIRONMENTAL ETHICS:
THE FOUNDATION OF A SUSTAINABLE SOCIETY

Outline

I. THE FRONTIER MENTALITY
    A. Roots of Our Attitudes Toward Nature
    B. The Technological Fix
    C. A More Personal Look
        1. Apathy
        2. The Self-Centered View
        3. Feelings of Insignificance
        4. Restricted Space-Time Values
    D. A Low-Synergy Society

II. SUSTAINABLE EARTH ETHICS
    A. Value Judgements and Decision Making

III. MAKING THE TRANSITION
    A. Three Approaches
    B. Some Attitudinal Changes Are Already Evident
    C. Avoiding Pitfalls

Objectives

After studying this chapter, the student should be able to:

1. Identify the out-of-date beliefs which underlie many of our environmental problems.
2. Characterize the *frontier mentality*, trace its development, and outline its environmental consequences.
3. Trace the roots of our attitudes toward nature via several historical and modern perspectives: the *Judeo-Christian tradition, biological imperialism*, and the *"I/not I"* model.
4. Understand and discuss the reasons for *societal* and *personal apathy* and *inertia* toward the adoption of more environmentally responsible ethics and lifestyles.
5. Discuss and use the *multiple cause and effect model* for analyzing major environmental issues.
6. Present several philosophical and/or personal arguments in support of the contention that our society has serious *obligations* to future generations.
7. Identify *obstacles* which currently prevent the adoption of a sustainable-society ethic.
8. Understand the necessity of ultimately adopting a sustainable-society system, and the ecological advantages of making the transition sooner rather than later.
9. Define *frontier mentality, biological imperialism, skin-encapsulated ego*, and *sustainable-society ethic*.
10. Distinguish among and compare the likelihood, desirability, and outcome of the following three approaches to making the sustainable-society transition: *bottom-up approach, top-down approach*, and *crisis approach*.

Lecture Notes

I. THE FRONTIER MENTALITY
- This is the *dominant paradigm* of modern society.
- The *frontier paradigm* has *three precepts*: the world's resource base and resiliency are limitless, humans are apart from nature, and nature is a rival to be conquered.
- This mentality, socialized and politicized, serves to justify the individual's pursuit of personal prosperity at the expense of ecosystem stability and diversity.

   A. Roots of Our Attitudes Toward Nature
   - Our attitude of mastery over nature can be traced to: the *Judeo-Christian* ethic, which exhorts us to exploit nature; our notion of *biological imperialism*, by which we explain our drive to dominate and exploit; and the psychological *"I/not I" model,* which sets us apart from nature.

   B. The Technological Fix
   - Out society has a nearly unshakable faith that *technology* can fix whatever we damage; such optimism is usually at odds with the facts and with critical thinking.

   C. A More Personal Look
   - The *outlooks* and *attitudes* of individuals often lead them to ignore or dismiss serious environmental problems.
      1. Apathy
      - Fostered by conditioning, a sense of powerlessness, and technological optimism, *apathy* causes us to shirk individual responsibility for environmental protection.
      2. The Self-Centered View
      - An excessively *self-centered* approach to life encourages consumerism and pursuit of personal material well-being at considerable environmental expense; it discourages personal involvement and sacrifice for environmental quality.
      3. Feelings of Insignificance
      - The belief that no one person's actions will make a significant difference may prevent us from taking individual actions that might collectively solve serious problems.
      4. Restricted Space-Time Values
      - Narrow *spatial* and *temporal* spheres of concern distort our values and contribute to our environmental disregard.

   D. A Low-Synergy Society
   - In a *low-synergy society*, individual interests work against the collective good; such a system is *unsustainable*.

II. SUSTAINABLE EARTH ETHICS
- Aldo Leopold's *A Sand County Almanac* first outlined and made a plea for a *land ethic*.
- Though valuable as an ideal goal, Leopold's land ethic offered little *guidance* for making the switch to a sustainable society.
- *Sustainable earth ethics* embraces the reverse of the tenets of the *frontier society*; it is based on *conservation, reuse* and *recycling, renewable resources,* and *population control,* and replaces human *arrogance* toward nature with *respect* and *restraint.*
- The sustainable earth ethic goes beyond the land ethic by giving *shape* to Leopold's *ideals*.

A. Value Judgements and Decision Making
- Our *values* strongly influence our *decision-making*, and the decisions we make profoundly affect the environment.
- Examples of value systems within which decisions are made include *utilitarianism, divine law*, and *natural rights*.

III. MAKING THE TRANSITION

A. Three Approaches
- There are *three approaches* to the development of a new social order and sustainable society.
- The *bottom-up* approach is initiated by a change in individual *attitudes* and *lifestyles*.
- The *top-down* approach calls for new *laws* and *regulations*.
- The *crisis* approach relies on the threat of imminent *disaster* to change policy and alter beliefs.

B. Some Attitudinal Changes Are Already Evident
- The change in attitude from "do more with more" to "do less with less" is beginning to take place, moving through intermediate stages such as "do more with less."

C. Avoiding Pitfalls
- Numerous *pitfalls* may impede our progress toward sustainability, including excessive *pessimism* and the resulting apathy and paralysis; excessive *optimism* and faith in technological fixes, which hinder personal responsibility and action; and *narrow, uncritical thinking* based on tradition and convention.

Critical Thinking Problems

1. Beginning with the ancient Greeks, many philosophers have identified two ethical roles in society: that of the *individual* and that of the *citizen*. In modern society, we also each have two identities: that of the *consumer* and that of the socially-responsible *citizen*. Do you make different choices regarding purchases, lifestyle, and politics as you switch from one role to the other? Are these roles *necessarily* conflicting? Identify several choices you made this week as a self-interested consumer and several which you made as a socially-responsible citizen. Which role predominates with you?

2. What specific barriers keep our society from adopting a long-term viewpoint necessary for planning a sustainable society? Consider in particular (a) our political system, including the average terms of office for our highest officials, and (b) our economic system, especially tax laws and incentives. Are there ways around these barriers?

Test Questions

Short Essay. Write a 250-300 word essay to answer each of the following questions.

1. Compare and contrast the frontier and sustainable-society mentalities. Be certain to look at how each views resources, our relation to the environment, and how we can solve our environmental problems.

2. Describe how apathy, self-centeredness, feelings of insignificance, and restricted space-time values affect our society's use of resources and levels of pollution.

3. List and discuss the most important ways to achieve a sustainable society. Before you do that, however, define a sustainable society. How is it different from our current society?

Suggested Readings and Resources Materials

Elliot and Gare, Eds. (1983). *Environmental Philosophy*. Pennsylvania: Pennsylvania State University Press. An excellent anthology of environmental philosophy articles.

Hargrove, E. (1989). *Foundations of Environmental Ethics*. New Jersey: Prentice-Hall. A good introduction, with emphasis on historical development of land-use attitudes and the environmental position.

Kamieniecki, O'Brien, and Clarke, Eds. (1986). *Controversies In Environmental Policy*. New York: SUNY Press. A helpful book for developing critical skills in this field. Covers both sides of environmental controversies.

Partridge, E., Ed. (1981). *Responsibility To Future Generations*. New York: Prometheus Books. A fine anthology of articles on our duties to posterity.

Rolston, H. III (1988). *Environmental Ethics*. Pennsylvania: Temple University Press. A wonderful combination of philosophy and literary skill by one of the founders of environmental ethics as a discipline in the U.S.

Taylor, P. (1986). *Respect For Nature*. New Jersey: Princeton University Press. Written from the biocentrist's point of view.

See also the quarterly journal *Environmental Ethics*, published by Environmental Philosophy, Inc., University of North Texas, Denton, Texas, for many good current articles in this field.

Videos: For ordering information, see Film/Video Index.

Energy and Morality. Amory Lovins and E.F. Schumacher look at redesigning human energy economics and ethics to accord with sustainablity. Contact Bullfrog Films.

Fence at Red Rim. A great test case for environmental ethics, this video explores the conflicts between pursuit of individual interest and societal/ecosystem good. Contact University of California Extension Media Center.

In Defense of Animals: A Portrait of Peter Singer. A video about animal rights and interests, showcasing one of the movement's better-known spokespersons. Contact Bullfrog Films.

The Global Brain. A video in which Peter Russell outlines the possibilities for humanity to use its collective intelligence as a "global brain" to reach our potential and discontinue destructive behavior. Contact The Video Project.

CHAPTER 20

ECONOMICS AND THE ENVIRONMENT

Outline

I. ECONOMICS AND THE ENVIRONMENT
   A. Economic Systems
   B. The Law of Supply and Demand
   C. Economic Measures: Beyond the GNP

II. THE ECONOMICS OF POLLUTION CONTROL
   A. Cost-Benefit Analysis and Pollution Control
   B. Who Should Pay for Pollution Control?
   C. Harnessing Market Forces to Protect the Environment
      1. Economic Disincentives
      2. Economic Incentives
      3. Permit Systems
      4. New Laws
   D. Environmental Regulations: Do They Impede Business?

III. THE ECONOMICS OF RESOURCE MANAGEMENT
   A. Time Preference
   B. Opportunity Cost
   C. Ethics

IV. DIFFERING PERSPECTIVES ON GROWTH AND THE FUTURE
   A. The Growth Issue
   B. Differing Perspectives on the Future

V. SUSTAINABLE ECONOMICS
   A. The Steady-State Economy
   B. Ethical Changes
   C. Population Control
   D. Nontraditional Proposals

VI. GLOBAL ECONOMIC CHALLENGES
   A. Challenges for the Developed Countries
   B. Challenges for the Less-Developed Nations
   C. Appropriate Technology and Sustainable Economic Development
   D. Making Sustainable Development Work

Objectives

After studying this chapter, the student should be able to:

1. Distinguish *descriptive* and *normative* economic systems.
2. Identify the *goals* of economics and the criteria each major economic system establishes for meeting those goals.

3. Discuss the role of the law of *supply and demand* in governing a market economy and its impacts on resources and conservation programs.
4. Outline an effective and efficient system for pollution control which utilizes various types of incentives, permits, and laws.
5. Understand the various economic and ethical factors which enter into our resource management decisions.
6. Present arguments in favor of adopting *long-term* versus *short-term* perspectives on the future.
7. Compare and contrast *growth-oriented* and *steady-state* economies with regard to social and environmental impact.
8. Identify and address the major economic challenges today for developed and less-developed nations as they move towards sustainability.
9. Define *appropriate technology* and discuss its role in global sustainable development.

Lecture Notes

I. ECONOMICS AND THE ENVIRONMENT
  - *Economics* is the study of the *production, distribution*, and *consumption* of goods and services.
  - Both *descriptive* and *normative economics* must be employed in any study of the relationship between economics and the environment.

  A. Economic Systems
    - Economics seeks to answer three questions: *what, how*, and *for whom* commodities should be produced.
    - These questions are answered differently in *command* and *market* economies; most nations' economies are *mixed*, with elements of both types integrated in them.

  B. The Law of Supply and Demand
    - *Price* is the main governor of behavior in a market economy; it is largely determined by *supply and demand*.
    - The *market price equilibrium* is the point at which supply and demand curves graphically intersect, and represents a price compromise between producers and consumers.
    - The *law of supply and demand* can have serious *implications* for the environment and may work against *conservation efforts*, as it fails to take into account the finite nature of many resources.

  C. Economic Measures: Beyond the GNP
    - *Gross national product* (GNP) is the most widely used measure of a nation's economic activity.
    - The GNP is *value-neutral* and counts wasteful or remedial expenditures as well as those genuinely contributory to standard of living improvement.
    - Subtracting these *disamenities* from the GNP yields *net economic welfare* (NEW), a more accurate measure of an economy's service to society. As pollution and congestion increase, the disparity between GNP and NEW increase.
    - Since GNP inherently favors *growth* and ignores *accumulated wealth*, it cannot guide or reflect the transition to a *sustainable economy*; similarly, by quantifying health statistics but ignoring total well-being, we fail to accurately measure a country's overall condition.

II. THE ECONOMICS OF POLLUTION CONTROL
- Traditionally, most economies have regarded pollution as an *economic externality*.
- In response to citizen complaint, some governments established *pollution control standards* which *internalized* the costs of industrial pollution.

A. Cost-Benefit Analysis and Pollution Control
- The *goal of cost-benefit analysis* is to maximize pollution control at minimum cost.
- *Problems* with cost-benefit analysis include the impossibility of *quantifying* certain costs and benefits, such as human life, pain and suffering, and aesthetic/intrinsic values; if not quantified, they cannot easily enter into the analysis.

B. Who Should Pay for Pollution Control?
- Either the *consumer*, the *taxpayer*, or *both* must bear the cost of pollution abatement programs; determining who should pay in a given situation is difficult and often controversial.
- Note that pollution control does not always *cost* but often *pays* the polluter, when all *direct, indirect*, and *repercussive costs* of pollution are figured in.

C. Harnessing Market Forces to Protect the Environment
- A number of *marketplace solutions* to pollution are under investigation.
1. Economic Disincentives
   - *Fines, taxes*, and *charges* can operate as *disincentives* to pollution.
2. Economic Incentives
   - These are *credits, tax breaks*, and *grants* which make pollution control economically appealing and encourage conservation.
3. Permit Systems
   - Flexible *marketable* and *tradeable permits* can achieve desired levels of pollution control while minimizing costs of compliance.
4. New Laws
   - *New legislation* to replace subsidies and depletion allowances which favor pollution and resource depletion can eliminate many environmentally destructive practices.

D. Environmental Regulations: Do They Impede Business?
- Claims that *environmental regulations* unnecessarily *delay projects, lower productivity*, and *reduce employment* are often grossly exaggerated or inaccurate, though a clean environment may, in fact, require some economic sacrifice in these areas.

III. THE ECONOMICS OF RESOURCE MANAGEMENT
- *Economic considerations* often influence our *behavior* and *decisions* regarding natural resources and pollution.

A. Time Preference
- *Time preference* refers to one's willingness to postpone a certain reward today for a greater reward in the future; it is influenced by *current needs, uncertainty of outcome, inflation rates*, and the *rate of return* on the postponed reward.
- With regard to natural resources, differing time preferences may lead to either *depletion* or *conservation strategies*.

B. Opportunity Cost
- This is the *cost* of *lost opportunities*; when high, it may discourage the adoption of conservation strategies, though the *reverse* is increasingly the case.

166

C. Ethics
- *Ethical considerations* are noneconomic factors which often affect our economic decisions.

IV. DIFFERING PERSPECTIVES ON GROWTH AND THE FUTURE

A. The Growth Issue
- The major *bias* of descriptive and normative economics is the tenet that *economic growth* is always desirable; this tenet rests upon the *frontier* belief that there is always *more* of everything needed to fuel such growth.
- The doctrine of *growth* requires an *ever-expanding population* and *ever-increasing per capita consumption*, both environmentally disastrous.

B. Differing Perspectives on the Future
- The *dividing line* between *short-term* and *long-term* is very different for *business people* and *politicians*, on one hand, and *environmentalists*, on the other.
- A *sustainable society* must redefine its primary goals in view of *long-term* considerations.

V. SUSTAINABLE ECONOMICS
- A *sustainable economy* will operate indefinitely within the limits imposed by nature; to achieve it will require *population control, value shifts*, and *political restructuring*.

A. The Steady-State Economy
- A sustainable economic system is a *steady-state economy*, based on sustainable production and consumption versus continual economic growth and resource depletion.

B. Ethical Changes
- Changes in *values* and our corresponding *ethics systems* will be necessary for abandonment of our current, wasteful policies and adoption of policies which foster sustainability.

C. Population Control
- A *sustainable economy* cannot be achieved without *population stabilization*, and *reduction*.

D. Nontraditional Proposals
- Several *radical/nontraditional changes* have been proposed to facilitate the shift to resource conservation and environmental protection in capitalist nations.

IV. GLOBAL ECONOMIC CHALLENGES

A. Challenges for the Developed Countries
- Developed countries must find ways to *stabilize* then *reduce population growth; reduce resource consumption; increase national self-sufficiency; repair, protect* and *conserve natural resources; cut pollution* sharply; support *global peace, cooperation*, and *sustainable development*; and, adopt a new *worldview* which values *sustainability* and promotes *individual responsibility*.

B. Challenges for the Less-Developed Nations
- *Population control, sustainable agriculture, improved standards of living* and *increased self-reliance* are appropriate goals for less-developed nations.
- *Sustainable development* programs can help those nations meet these goals.

C. Appropriate Technology and Sustainable Economic Development
  • Sustainable practices can be promoted by *appropriate policy* and carried out through use of *appropriate technology*, that is, technology geared to the human needs and environmental conditions of the country in which it is used.

D. Making Sustainable Development Work
  • International development programs have, on the whole, been neither *economically* nor *socially* successful; often, they have been outright *damaging*.
  • These shortcomings can be addressed by development programs which take a *comprehensive, long-term, ecological view* at existing problems and possible solutions.

Case Studies

In Africa, Wildlife Pays Its Own Way

In Zimbabwe, wildlife management has taken a pragmatic turn that disheartens many wildlife advocates, but may help preserve important wildlife species. The basic idea behind Zimbabwe's new wildlife management policy is to turn wildlife into a valuable resource, like oil or wheat. If the animals can bring in revenue, whether from hunters, photographic safaris, or from meat production, then people may have more incentive to preserve their habitat and their numbers.

This radical idea that wildlife must pay its own way has become commonplace in Africa's Zimbabwe. The country's landscape is dotted with "game farms" in which wild animals are raised alongside cattle and wheat. On these game farms, trophy hunters pay large sums to hunt "wild" animals. In parks, government wildlife managers may kill surplus animals and sell their hides or their meats locally. The sales help finance wildlife protection and prevent species from overpopulating their limited range.

David Cumming, former executive director of Zimbabwe's Department of National Parks and Wildlife Management, said, "If wildlife can be treated as a national resource, then it can be used and managed on a sustainable basis. And if land owners can derive benefits from those resources, they will look after the animals. Otherwise, people will regard wild creatures as nuisances and get rid of them."

This new and sometimes startling wildlife management program was first used in the 1960s when the country of Zimbabwe was called Rhodesia. The government set aside numerous national parks and game reserves to protect animals. Thus, while elephants were being slaughtered in outlying areas, they bred prolifically in the parks and game preserves. Unfortunately, the large animals began decimating their own habitat. Wildlife biologists suggested that the parks cull surplus animals to protect the habitat. At first, wildlife advocates were appalled, but many gradually came to realize the merit of this scheme. For instance, by keeping the number of elephants at about 40,000, the parks department prevents the animals from destroying their own food source and from damaging the habitat of other creatures. Each year about 1500 elephants are killed in Zimbabwe. This brings revenue to local villages.

The success of the parks department led to the Parks and Wildlife Act of 1975. It committed the country to conserving and using its resources rather than simply preserving them. Today, 12.7% of Zimbabwe's land area is park land or biological reserve. Except for the endangered black rhino, most other animal species are flourishing. Their numbers are kept in check by culling or translocation to other areas.

The private sector is also taking an active role in wildlife management, since wildlife can be competitive economically with livestock. Many people will pay large sums of money just to see or to hunt wildlife. Studies by the parks department show that wildlife can yield 1.5 to 4 times as much revenue per acre as cattle. Wildlife are less damaging to the environment as well.

The grim current outlook for agriculture has helped turn many ranchers and farmers into wildlife managers. Today more than 500 land owners have joined the wildlife producers association in Zimbabwe, and many now let impalas, wildebeest and other animals roam on their land.

Wildlife ranching conserves wildlife, protects habitat, and helps support local people. Unfortunately, many of the current wildlife ranchers in Zimbabwe are relatively wealthy. As a result, the parks department has launched a program to help foster wildlife ranching among the two million people who live in remote rural areas of the country where poverty is endemic.

Several years ago park officials and the Shangaan tribespeople in Southeast Zimbabwe were locked in a battle over elephants. Elephants were crossing from parks and raiding the crops of the farmers. Farmers sneaked into the park at night to kill the marauding elephants.

In 1982 a cattle rancher, Clive Stockil, stepped in. He convinced the tribesmen that if they let the elephants flourish on the land, they could earn money by culling them. He then helped the parks department establish quotas. Soon the Shangaan were hosting trophy hunters, offering their expertise as trackers, meat processors and skinners. Within a year the rate of poaching fell by 90% and the tribesmen began earning substantial amounts of money.

Even though wildlife are flourishing throughout the country, the black rhino still remains imperiled. The problem is that the rhino horn is extremely valuable, often worth more than $10,000 each. Poachers frequently sneak into parks and kill the rhinos for this valuable horn. To prevent this needless slaughter, the parks department has authorized its wildlife managers to shoot on sight any poachers. Despite this stringent policy, 404 of the estimated 700 black rhinos in the Zambezi river valley have been slaughtered since the anti-poaching patrol began. As a result, Zimbabwe is trying another approach, capturing the rhinoceroses and moving them to safer areas. More than 200 have been removed from the river valley in the last 3 years. Some have even been moved to private ranches. Zimbabwe officials hope that the rhinos and the rest of the nation's animals will attract enough tourists, photographers, and safari hunters to bring in much needed foreign exchange. This money, they hope, will continue efforts to save wildlife.

Outside disapproval of the country's philosophy, however, could undermine the scheme. Says David Cummings, "If there is resistance to these concepts in the U.S. or Europe, it can block the markets for wildlife utilization, and then those conservationists will be contributing to land degradation instead of wildlife."

Adapted from: Achiron, M. (1988). "Making Wildlife Pay Its Way." *International Wildlife*, Vol. 18, No. 5, pp. 46-51.

Critical Thinking Problems

1. Are there some things in life that are priceless, i.e. that are so valuable that they *must* be protected no matter the cost or economic sacrifice? If so, are they universally recognized?

2. Libertarians argue that it is too much government regulation, not too little, which has produced the environmental mess we are in today. They believe that in a truly *free market* economy, where

each person bears full financial responsibility for the effects of his activities, pollution and depletion would be minimized as individuals would see the need to practice sustainability to protect their own future interests. Critically assess this argument.

3. Can a free market or capitalist economy ever be fully compatible with the ideals of justice? Does justice help guide the "invisible hand" of our economy?

Test Questions

Multiple choice. Each of the following questions has one correct answer. Circle the letter corresponding to the choice you think best answers the question.

D   1.   The measure of the value of goods and services produced by a nation in a given year is called:

     a.   the net wealth.
     b.   measure of economic wealth.
     c.   gross national index.
     d.   gross national product.

E   2.   The law of supply and demand:

     a.   accurately reflects the short-term economic picture.
     b.   says that prices, supply, and demand for goods are all interdependent.
     c.   poorly predicts the long-term economic picture because it fails to take into account the finite nature of some resources.
     d.   b & c
     e.   all of the above

D   3.   One's willingness to give up some current income for income of potentially greater return in the future is:

     a.   often based on the size of the future return.
     b.   often based on short-term monetary needs.
     c.   called the depletion strategy.
     d.   a & b
     e.   b & c

A   4.   Most economic systems:

     a.   ignore the external costs of pollution and technology.
     b.   incorporate the external costs of pollution and technology so that products reflect the total costs.
     c.   concentrate on external costs and ignore internal costs.
     d.   a & b
     e.   b & c

C   5.   A steady-state economy:

   a. seeks growth in GNP.
   b. pays little attention to product durability.
   c. relies on recycling and conservation.
   d. emphasizes centralized manufacturing of goods.

Fill in the Blank. For each of the following questions, fill in the blank with the appropriate word or phrase.

1.   In a _____ economy, the government largely dictates production and distribution goals.

2.   The Law of _____ states that most things that people want are limited.

3.   The _____ _____ _____ is a measure derived by adjusting the GNP to remove the cost of pollution and other activities that do not improve the quality of life.

4.   _____ economics is the objective study of economic activity.

5.   Economics concerns itself with two things: _____, such as minerals and labor, and _____, the goods and services produced.

Answers: 1. command   2. Scarcity   3. net economic welfare   4. Positive   5. inputs, outputs

Short Essay. Write a 250-300 word essay to answer each of the following questions.

1.   How do we assess wealth in this country and compare countries with one another? Are our measures of wealth accurate or valuable? Why or why not?

2.   Draw graphs representing the laws of supply and demand. Discuss how increasing and decreasing supply affect price when the demand is constant.

3.   The conservation and the depletion strategies are radically different approaches to how we treat resources. What factors determine our choice of strategies?

4.   What are the three options for payment of environmental costs? Under what circumstances is each valid, in your view?

Suggested Readings and Resource Materials

Chandler, William. *The Changing Role of the Market in National Economies.* Washington, DC: WorldWatch Institute.

Daly, Herman and John Cobb (1990). *For the Common Good: Redirecting the Economy toward Community, the Environment, and a Sustainable Future.* Boston: Beacon Press. An economist and a theologian attempt to examine the whole economic system and point it in a new direction good for economy and environment alike.

Newland, Kathleen. *Productivity: The New Economic Context.* Washington, DC: WorldWatch Institute.

Videos: For ordering information, see Film/Video Index.

A Sense of Place: Tourism, Development, and Preserving the Environment. Looks at conflicting needs and goals in Lake George, NY. Contact Umbrella Films.

Conservation of the Southern Rainforest. Focuses on the development of controlled tourism as an economic alternative to unstainable development in developing nations. Contact Umbrella Films.

Small Is Beautiful: Impressions of Fritz Schumacher. Interviews with the noted British economist. Contact National Film Board of Canada.

Pollution: How Much Is a Clean Environment Worth? Examines externalities and "optimum" pollution levels. Contact The University of Minnesota.

CHAPTER 21

GOVERNMENT AND THE ENVIRONMENT

Outline

I. GOVERNMENT: AN OVERVIEW
   A. Forms of Government
   B. The Role of Government in Environmental Protection

II. POLITICAL DECISION MAKING: WHO CONTRIBUTES?
   A. Government Officials
   B. The Public
   C. Special Interest Groups

III. SOME BARRIERS TO SUSTAINABILITY AND SOME SUGGESTIONS
   A. Lack of Consensus
      1. Research
      2. Education
   B. Crisis Politics
      1. Proactive and Reactive Government
      2. Long-Range Planning and Follow Up
   C. Limited Planning Horizons
   D. Inadequate Land-Use Planning
      1. Sustainability Through Land-Use Planning
      2. Zoning
      3. Agroecological Zones

IV. A SUSTAINABLE WORLD COMMUNITY
   A. West Germany's Green Party: An Ecological Approach to Politics
   B. Achieving a Global Sustainable Society
   C. Global Resource Sharing: Is It a Good Idea?

V. CHAPTER SUPPLEMENT. A PRIMER ON ENVIRONMENTAL LAW
   A. National Environmental Policy Act
   B. Environmental Protection Agency
   C. Evolution of U.S. Environmental Law
   D. Principles of Environmental Law
      1. Statutory Law
      2. Common Law
   E. Problems in Environmental Lawsuits
   F. Resolving Environmental Disputes Out of Court

Objectives

After studying this chapter, the student should be able to:

1. Compare forms of *government* and their roles in environmental protection.
2. Specify the roles of *government officials*, the *public*, and *special interest groups* in political decision making.
3. Identify the major *barriers* to sustainability and offer suggestions for their removal or circumvention.
4. Distinguish *proactive* and *reactive* government policies and approaches.
5. Characterize a *sustainable world community* and offer ideas for its achievement.
6. Outline the development of U.S. *environmental law* at the *local*, *state*, and *federal* levels.
7. Define *statutory* and *common law* and identify the role of each in environmental protection.

Lecture Notes

I. GOVERNMENT: AN OVERVIEW

    A. Forms of Government
*   In general, free market economies predominate in *democratic nations*, while command economies are found in nations with *communist* or *socialist* governments.

    B. The Role of Government in Environmental Protection
*   Governments regulate activities and protect the environment through *taxes, expenditures*, and *regulations*.
*   *Taxes* help regulate behavior and raise funds for *government expenditures*, such as pollution-control project grants and procurements programs; in poor countries, such funds are scarce.
*   *Regulations* take the form of federal *laws* or *agency-promulgated regulations* which govern specific activities.

II. POLITICAL DECISION MAKING: WHO CONTRIBUTES?

    A. Government Officials
*   *Government officials* have the most power in communist nations, but often have final say on certain policies in any type of government.

    B. The Public
*   *Voters* influence policy in democratic nations by selecting representatives and by communicating their priorities and concerns to those in office. Even communist governments are somewhat responsive to public sentiments.

    C. SPECIAL INTEREST GROUPS
*   *Special interest groups*, such as automakers and environmental organizations, can exert leveraged and sometimes disproportionate influence on policymakers, through PAC's and lobbying.
*   *Environmental groups* also affect public policy through public displays, educational materials, awareness-raising activities, pollution monitoring, legal challenges, protests, and interventions.

III. SOME BARRIERS TO SUSTAINABILITY AND SOME SUGGESTIONS

  A. Lack of Consensus
   * *Lack of consensus* or agreement about goals and priorities sometimes prevents positive action.
   1. Research
      * By reducing empirical uncertainty, *research* can help establish goals for long-range planning.
   2. Education
      * *Education* can help galvanize the public in commitment to solving environmental problems.

  B. Crisis Politics
   * *Reacting* to urgent, immediately pressing problems, rather than *proacting* to deal with important long-term problems, is characteristic of *crisis politics*.
   1. Proactive and Reactive Government
      * *Reactive governments* primarily address *urgent, immediate issues* with proposals for *remedial action*.
      * *Proactive government* takes a *long-term outlook* and aims to *prevent*, rather than solve, problems.
      * Most governments mix reactive and proactive policies and approaches, but *reaction* predominates in modern political systems.
   2. Long-Range Planning and Follow-Up
      * Better *research* and *education* should lead to increased emphasis on *long-range planning* and *follow-ups* in the form of enforcing, updating, and revising; the *Global 2000 Report to the President* is an excellent example of a long-range plan.

  C. Limited Planning Horizons
   * The *planning horizon* of political decision makers is unduly shortened by budget periods, turns in office, and re-election concerns; most environmental protection measures require longer planning horizons and payback periods.

  D. Inadequate Land-Use Planning
   * Poor or inadequate *land-use planning* puts land to unsustainable uses and can be ruinous.
   1. Sustainability Through Land-Use Planning
      * Proper land-use planning manages resources for maximum *sustainability* and *long-term productivity*.
   2. Zoning
      * *Zoning* is the main tool of land-use planners; it can be used in conjunction with *differential tax assessment laws* and purchase of *development rights* to protect resources.
   3. Agroecological Zones
      * These are identified on zoning maps, which could be used to protect farmland and foster agricultural *sustainability*.

IV. A SUSTAINABLE WORLD COMMUNITY
   * Changes needed to move towards worldwide sustainablity include *abandonment of war economies, international cooperation and sharing*, more investments in *environmentally and socially responsible projects*, and *population control.*

A. West Germany's Green Party: An Ecological Approach to Politics
- The *Greens* are a political party actively pushing for a proactive, long-range approach to government; their goal is creation of a *sustainable society.*

B. Achieving a Global Sustainable Society
- *International cooperation*, as exhibited by the U.N., E.E.C., and I.W.C., is necessary to achieve this goal.

C. Global Resource Sharing: Is It a Good Idea?
- While *personally appealing*, efforts to achieve sustainability through global natural resource sharing may be *ecologically misguided; knowledge* may instead be the most valuable resource to be shared.

V. CHAPTER SUPPLEMENT. A PRIMER ON ENVIRONMENTAL LAW

A. National Environmental Policy Act
- *NEPA* is a landmark piece of U.S. environmental legislation which introduced requirements for *environmental impact statements* and set a goal of minimum environmental impact for all federal projects.

B. Environmental Protection Agency
- Founded in 1970, the *EPA* manages many of the major environmental laws written by Congress and conducts research, provides grants, and otherwise influences policy and action related to environmental issues.

C. Evolution of U.S. Environmental Law
- *State* and *federal environmental laws* gradually evolved from scattered *local ordinances* which limited activities of a few for the good of all.
- *Conflicts* between neighboring *municipalities* necessitated pollution controls at the *state* level.
- Because pollution crosses state lines, *interstate conflicts* arose; in response, environmental legislation was enacted at the *federal* level.
- The federal government is best suited to regulate in situations requiring *uniform standards* and large *expenditures.*

D. Principles of Environmental Law
  1. Statutory Law
     - *Statutory laws* state *broad principles*, for which specific standards are set by EPA or other agencies.
  2. Common Law
     - *Common law* is a body of *unwritten rules and principles* derived from countless legal precedents.
     - Through common law, competing interests are weighed and, ideally, fairly protected.
     - Most common law cases are decided on the basis of *two legal principles: nuisance* and *negligence.*

E. Problems in Environmental Lawsuits
- *Burdens of proof, statutes of limitations*, and *out-of-court settlements* have all presented legal problems to those trying to settle environmental lawsuits.

F. Resolving Environmental Disputes Out of Court
    • *Mediation* or *dispute resolution* is increasingly used to settle environmental disputes out of court; it is less costly, less time-consuming, and less adversarial.

Case Study

The New Federalism: Finding the Balance

Government itself may stand in the way of building a sustainable society. Because of its size, the federal government can become insensitive to local problems and can prescribe solutions that are not well suited to individual regions. You may recall from Chapter 20 that one of the proposals for building a sustainable society was selective decentralization of some industries. Society may also benefit from some selective governmental decentralization.

President Reagan's "new federalism" was just such an attempt. By reducing federal funding of cities and local projects, the federal government shifted more and more power to the states and local governments. This so-called "new federalism" offers several potential advantages and disadvantages. Achieving success lies in the balance: finding the optimal mix between federal and local control, especially in regard to resource and other environmental issues.

Advocates of more decentralized government see the partial shift in power to the states and local governments as a way of building a more self-reliant and responsible society, one that lives within the limits of nature. They argue that people will feel less alienated from government and more willing to participate in community decisions when more decisions are made locally.

Forced to rely more on their own tax revenue and less on federal support, communities may turn to conservation and recycling to cut costs of services. In Englewood, Colorado, for instance, city fathers voted to burn methane produced at sewage treatment plants to generate electricity to run the sewage treatment plants. In other cities, waste heat from power plants could be captured to heat office buildings or homes. Sewage sludge is used elsewhere to fertilize corn, which is fed to cattle or sold to local markets. Instead of building new water projects, some governments are implementing water conservation measures. Left to their own devices, local governments may find that energy conservation and local renewable sources, such as biomass and solar, are less expensive than coal-fired power plants.

A community that lives within the limits posed by its economic and natural resources is more easily sustained than one that imports energy, natural resources, food, and goods from afar. Such a community provides the essential goods and services within a limited environment and is called an essential community.

A shift from centralized federal governments to decentralized essential communities has its disadvantages--hence the need for finding the optimal mix of governance. One of the major problems is that local governments generally lack money and may be influenced more heavily by businesses that push for relaxation of pollution laws. Decentralization, in other words, is no guarantee of wise resource use. (As you saw in the Chapter Supplement, federal rules and regulations evolved because of inadequate state and local controls.) Another problem is that local governments rarely have the financial resources needed to sponsor feasibility studies on pollution control, recycling projects, alternative energy systems, and such.

Truly, a proper balance between local and federal power is important in developing a sustainable society. The federal government must be ready to assist communities in finding the most cost-effective and least resource-intensive approaches to providing services. Federal demonstration programs, standards for pollution control, and research are all essential for a sustainable local government to evolve, for such work would help standardize rules and regulations.

Critical Thinking Problems

1. Is truly enlightened, sustainability-oriented land-use planning compatible with the ideals of democratic government?

2. Must individual, short-term interests *always* conflict with collective, long-term interests? If so, is there any one system of government equipped to reconcile the two?

3. Imagine that you have just been appointed benevolent dictator of the universe. You can decree one law, and one law only, to govern all of society. Assuming you wish to act in the best overall, long-term interests of humanity, what would that law be?

Test Questions

Short Essay. Write a 250-300 word essay to answer each of the following questions.

1. Describe the ways that governments can affect environmental protection.

2. Discuss the role of government officials, the general public, and special interest groups in policy making.

3. Describe the major obstacles to political change toward a sustainable society, and ways to overcome them. Which of your solutions are likely to be enacted within your lifetime?

4. Global resource sharing is viewed by many as an important step in building a sustainable society. Discuss both sides of the issue and describe your view.

Chapter Supplement. Primer on Environmental Law

Fill in the Blank. For each of the following questions, fill in the blank with the appropriate word or phrase.

1. The National _____ _____ Act requires all federal agencies to prepare an environmental impact statement for their projects or projects they fund.

2. The executive branch office, the Council ___ _____ _____, publishes an annual report on the environment and advises the President on environmental matters.

3. Many environmental cases are tried on the basis of _____ law, the body of unwritten rules and principles derived from thousands of years of legal decisions dating back to ancient times.

4. _____ are a class of wrongs that arise from the unreasonable or unlawful use of one's own property if it injures another person.

5. A person acting in an unreasonable manner and causing damage or injury to another is said to be _____ in the eyes of the law.

Answers: 1. Environmental Policy   2. on Environmental Quality   3. common   4. Nuisances
5. negligent

Short Essay. Write a 250-300 word essay to answer each of the following questions.

1. Debate the statement: Environmental laws should be turned over to the states. How would a movement of this nature fit into the evolution of environmental law? Would the effect of such actions on the whole be good or bad?

2. Discuss the ways in which the Environmental Protection Agency has worked to increase environmental protection.

3. How can land-use planning help us build a sustainable society?

Suggested Readings and Resource Materials

Borrelli, Peter, Ed. (1988). *Crossroads: Environmental Priorities for the Future.* Washington, DC: Island Press. An in-depth examination of the environmental movement's successes and failures, along with prescriptions for the future.

Brown, Janet (1990). *In the U.S. Interest: Resources, Growth and Security in the Developing World.* Westview Press. Fully explores the economic and political consequences of population growth, pollution, and resource depletion.

Brown, Lester and P. Shaw. *Six Steps to a Sustainable Society.* Washington, DC: WorldWatch Institute.

Cahn, Robert, Ed. (1985). *An Environmental Agenda for the Future.* Washington, DC: Island Press. Advice from the heads of the major conservation organizations in the world.

Comp, T. Allan, Ed. (1988). *Blueprint for the Environment.* New York: Howe Bros. A checklist for federal action and a guide to the workings of our government on environmental issues.

Deudney, Daniel. *Whole-Earth Security: A Geopolitics of Peace.* Washington, DC: WorldWatch Institute.

Eckholm, Erik. *The Dispossessed of the Earth: Land Reform and Sustainable Development.* Washington, DC: WorldWatch Institute.

Newland, Kathleen. *Refugees: The New International Politics of Displacement.* Washington, DC: WorldWatch Institute.

Renner, Michael. *National Security: The Economic and Environmental Dimensions.* Washington, DC: WorldWatch Institute.

Western and Pearl, Eds. (1989). *Conservation for the Twenty-First Century.* Washington, DC: Island Press. Brings together for the concerned individual diverse approaches to conservation now and in the next century.

Videos: For ordering information, see Film/Video Index.

Environment Under Fire: Ecology and Politics in Central America. An in-depth look at the links between poverty, war, and environmental destruction. Contact The Video Project.

FILM/VIDEO INDEX: Sources

The following is a partial list of sources for films and videos which deal with topics typically discussed in an environmental science class. The source for each film or video mentioned in this guide is included here, as are several other sources from which relevant visual materials may be obtained. Please contact the organizations for catalogs and ordering information.

ABC Wide World of Learning, Inc.
1330 Avenue of the Americas
New York, NY 10019   (212) 887-5706

Appalshop Films
Box 743 A
Whitesburg, KY 41858   (606) 633-0108

Barfuss Films
Schiller Strasse 52
78 Freiburg
Federal Republic of Germany

BBC Enterprises
Education and Training Sales Dept.
Woodlands
Wood Lane
London W12 OTT
England

Bullfrog Films
Oley, PA 19547
(215) 779-8226; (800) 543-FROG

Churchill Films
662 North Robertson Boulevard
Los Angeles, CA 90069

Cine Research Associates
32 Fisher Avenue
Boston, MA 02120   (617) 442-9756

Coronet Film & Video
108 Wilmot Road
Deerfield, IL 60015   (800) 621-2131

Environmental Media Association
10536 Culver Boulevard
Culver City, CA 90232 (213) 559-9334

Films for the Humanities & Sciences, Inc.
P.O. Box 2053
Princeton, NJ 08543   (609) 542-1128; (800) 257-5726

Hartley Film Foundation

Cat Rock Road
Cos Cob, CT 06807
International Film Bureau, Inc.
332 South Michigan Avenue
Chicago, IL 60604   (312) 427-4545

National Audubon Video/Inovision
P.O. Box 576
Itasca, IL 60143   (800) 523-5503

National Film Board of Canada
International Distribution Division
P.O. Box 6100, Station A
Montreal, Quebec,
Canada H3C 3H5   (514) 283-9440

National Wildlife Federation
1400 16th Street, N.W.
Washington, DC 20036 (800) 432-6564

Nature Conservancy
1815 North Lynn Street
Arlington, VA 22209 (703) 841-8745

NOVA
NOVA's videos are distributed by Coronet Film & Video.

Project Lighthawk
P.O. Box 8163
Santa Fe, NM 87504   (505) 982-9656

Richter Productions
330 West 42nd Street
New York, NY 10036 (212) 947-1395

Television Trust for the Environment
46 Charlotte Street
London W1P 11R
England

The Cinema Guild
1697 Broadway
New York, NY 10019 (212) 246-5522

The Council for Chemical Research
One Bethlehem Plaza, Suite 911
Bethlehem, PA 18018 (215) 866-7725

The Population Institute
110 Maryland Avenue, N.E.
Washington, DC 20002

The University of Minnesota
University Film and Video
1313 Fifth Street, S.E., Suite 108
Minneapolis, MN 55414 (612) 627-4270

The Video Project
5332 College Avenue, Suite 101
Oakland, CA 94618 (415) 655-9050

Umbrella Films
60 Blake Road
Brookline, MA 02146 (617) 277-6639

UNEP Information Service
Audio Visual Unit
P.O. Box 30552
Nairobi, Kenya
U.S. Contact: Joan Martin-Brown, UNEP
1889 F Street, N. W.
Washington, DC 20036 (202) 289-8456

University of California Extension Media Center
2176 Shattuck Avenue
Berkeley, CA 94704 (415) 642-1340

WETA Visions
WETA/TV
Box 2626
Washington, DC   (800) 445-1964

WGBH
125 Western Avenue
Boston, MA 02134 (805) 685-9685